THE GIFTS THEY BRING

Our Debt to the Mentally Retarded

THE JOHN DAY SPECIAL EDUCATION BOOKS

THE GIFTS
THEY BRING

Our Debt to the Mentally Retarded

PEARL S. BUCK

GWENETH T. ZARFOSS

THE JOHN DAY COMPANY

NEW YORK

Library of Congress Catalogue Card Number: 65-13742

MANUFACTURED IN THE UNITED STATES OF AMERICA

CONTENTS

PREFACE

Out of the shadows of yesterday the faces of children appear.

They are the special children, the ones whose minds have not developed as they could have. Behind each child is a family saddened because the child lives. Children are for joy; they are the carriers of life. But these children are not such. Innocent as babies all their lives long, they are nevertheless a burden, the cause of unutterable sorrow, of tears and heartache, of separation of their families from others.

Who are they? They are the children who never grow. They are the mentally retarded.

Are there many?

One out of every one thousand children born is seriously retarded. Three out of every one thousand are unlikely to progress beyond a mental age of seven years. Twenty-six out of every one thousand are more or less affected, so that they are slow of mind.

Why should there be so many?

Because there are many ways in which nature can go wrong. The human fetus is a tender thing, a bit of membrane, a gossamer of potential life. Yet it has a portentous role to play. After the first stir at the meeting of the two essential elements, male and female, the fetus must proceed at a certain pace, step by step, toward the climax of birth. It clings to a protecting womb by no more than a tendril; it absorbs nourishment from the mother but it creates itself, building upon the given ancestral base a new human being—bones, blood, flesh, hair and skin, all new. Yet each step of growth is prescribed by the history of the human race.

If every step is taken rightly, a perfect child is born, bringing joy and fulfillment. If there is a misstep, however slight, if there is a slowing in the process, if the ancestral base is imperfect, if the nourishment is inadequate, if a disease germ attacks, or a wrong chemical is introduced, a different child is born. Nature insists upon creation, the work goes on somehow, but how sad is the result! The child is twisted, the shape tortured perhaps into monstrosity, limbs lacking, bones crooked, or, in subtler more heart-breaking imagination, the precious brain, that jewel, that treasure within its box, is hopelessly injured. When the brain is imperfect, then all goes wrong, for then the mind is not properly housed. It cannot take command. It leaps and falters; it is at the mercy of the body; it is imprisoned; it cannot grow. We say that the child is retarded.

Or sadder still, the child may be perfectly born, and disease may attack after birth. Encephalitis, meningitis, high fevers too prolonged, may damage the cells of the brain, a physical damage, yet injuring the mind. We say again that the child is retarded.

What shall we do with these millions of retarded children? They are being born every day. What have we done with them in the past? Until very recently we have done nothing with them and for them except hide them. We kept them hidden in the homes where they were born or we put them into institutions because we did not know what to do with them. They created problems we could not solve. We could not answer the inanswerable *why,* either for ourselves as a cry out of our own broken hearts or as a question that others asked.

Yet there is nothing new about these innocent children. They have not appeared suddenly in our own times. Since the race of man began, there have been these who did not grow. Once they were made into jesters and fools for kings, slaves in households. Or they were maimed as beggars and used as thieves, misunderstood and often mistreated even in the privacy of their own family circles. In later years they were put away into institutions, and great buildings were erected at vast public expense, their emptiness soon filled to overflow with retarded children of all ages.

Nor has this entirely changed. Doctors may still advise the parents of a newborn child who is obviously defective to place him at once in an institution. Sometimes the mother never even sees the child. She has carried him with her in the closest of human relationships for many months, yet when he is born he is snatched away from her. Who can estimate the damage done to the mother in having her emotions thus stopped, the natural flow of outgoing love dammed, only to find its later expression in feelings of guilt and despair? And what of the child, robbed of parents' love and the security of home and family only to be consigned to strangers upon whom he is now wholly dependent? In addition to his own inadequacy, he must bear the heavy burden of lovelessness and so of going his pitiful way through life alone.

It is a human situation insupportable for the civilized mind to contemplate, and within the last two decades such minds have done much to change it. The movement began with the parents of retarded children. Nature is indiscriminate. The accidents of human development fall upon the brilliant and the able as often as they do on lesser persons. Rare indeed is the family anywhere in the world that has no retarded child somewhere within its history. It is not surprising, therefore, that intelligent parents were the first to realize that their retarded children had the same rights as other children to reach their highest potential and furthermore that they themselves must take leadership in establishing these rights for their retarded children. Once convinced, they organized, in local groups and then nationally, to present their case to the public—and with remarkable success. Today mental retardation is no longer a shameful secret. It is recognized as a condition for which there are many causes, some of them physical, and a good beginning has been made through scientific research to isolate and discover these causes.

Beyond this, much is being done to help these parents care for and teach their children. Our public libraries, which for so long contained little if anything on the subject, now provide volumes written expressly for parents and teachers of retarded children. Free and inexpensive pamphlets for the guidance of the families and teachers of retarded are continually being distributed by both public and private agencies. Individual experiences related by warmhearted, understanding parents about their acceptance of a retarded child appear in periodicals and magazines. Communities are developing plans to put into practice the carefully prepared recommendations of the President's Panel on Mental Retardation. In short, parents no longer struggle alone with their problems. We are now engaged in a national program to combat mental retardation. The National Broadcasting System, for example, has devoted an entire week of its early morning *Today* program to newly developed techniques for the care of retarded persons.

In some quarters one hears complaints, of course, that the time, effort, and money needed for the care and training of the retarded, in addition to the vast sums essential for research, had better be spent on developing the minds of normal and especially gifted children, since they are more likely to make individual contributions to society. To this we can only reply that it cannot be either–or. It must be both. All children must have their chances. In the first place, no human being can be relegated because of race, religion, or handicap, without endangering the rights of all. It was Hitler who first proved this to be true when in the name of a utilitarian philosophy he had put to death the retarded children in institutions. This philosophy eventually led to the destruction of other groups, so that in the end millions of people were murdered. The power of death is second only to the power of creating life.

In the second place, we must consider the constantly increasing cost of lifelong care for the person unable to care for himself. None but the wealthy can afford this care and public funds must therefore be provided, funds which could be used in much more productive ways than merely keeping human beings alive. Such funds can be put to use in prevention, insofar as possible, of retardation through research, thus lessening the number of dependent persons. Research is slow, however, even though the result, once achieved, is striking and immediate. And it is true that there will always be some who cannot be helped even by research. These, the permanently retarded, must be helped out of total dependence. They, too, must be trained as far as possible to become tax producers rather than consumers.

We do not wish to emphasize the financial importance of such independence. Rather let us emphasize the incalculable value to all of us in the continuing effort of preventing mental retardation in the first place, and in the second place of seeing that the retarded are given full opportunity for development and, insofar as they can, the satisfying experience of being able to fulfill themselves. In the process we will discover not how much we do for them, but how much they do for us. That is the surprise; that is the reward. Research, begun for the prevention of retardation, is already revealing sources of benefit for all human beings. Teaching methods developed for the slow to learn, even for the apparently unteachable, are proving useful in teaching other children and adults. In short, we are finding that the retarded are not essentially different from other persons, except that they are slower in varying degrees, and arrive at their maximum at different levels. Our interest grows with discovery, and it becomes important to clarify, even in this still very preliminary stage of work with the retarded, some of the benefits they have already bestowed upon us.

Out of such discovery and interest this book was begun. Our first step was to inquire if such a report had already been made. If so, we have not been able to find it. In all the avalanche of material now being poured out by professionals in the field of the mentally retarded, little evidence has been collected to prove that the retarded have influenced our present activities and way of life. Yet for years men and women have agreed in theory that the study of abnormal behavior leads to a better understanding of the normal. In reality, it is easy to understand why this has not been done. The entire focus of our attention has been on *what we could do for the retarded,* not on what they do for us. It is a learning process in which we are now engaged as we write this book.

THE GIFTS THEY BRING

Our Debt to the Mentally Retarded

CHAPTER I

YESTERDAY, TODAY
AND TOMORROW

Man of all ages and cultures is confronted with solving the same primary questions: how to supply his own needs and how to supply the needs of others. We have had to discover that each human being, although he has much in common with his fellowmen, is unique, and that this is true even of identical twins. Each is a person and must be treated as such. Each has individual needs. A normal person with diabetes requires a special diet. A blind child needs special education. A man without legs must be given a specific type of employment. Furthermore, in relation to our needs it is necessary to discover and accept a cause. Nothing just happens. It is as difficult for a normal child to function well if his eyes are itching because they are strained as it is for us to enjoy good health if we are disturbed because of the physical or mental problem of someone we love. In this slow process of learning about our own needs we have

made the grave mistake of thinking that the needs of retarded persons differ radically from ours. We have also
assumed that the needs of *all* retarded persons are the same.

Let us therefore put down an axiom: the fundamental
needs of both children and adults, be they normal or retarded, handicapped or non-handicapped, *are the same.*
Some of these are emotional needs. We are born with them
just as we are born with physical needs, but we are not
born already knowing the best ways to satisfy them. This
we have to learn because each need affects us in different
ways at different periods throughout our entire lives. All
are directly connected to our physical needs and work together with them as parts of our whole being. No part can
be ignored without causing damage to the entire personality.

As William Trombley said about adoption in his "Babies
Without Homes":

> Many unwanted Negro infants stay for as long as six months
> in Cook County Hospital's nursery. There they wither for
> lack of the loving care all babies need, and no hospital no
> matter how well intentioned, can provide. After six months
> many are shunted off to institutions for the mentally re-
> tarded, because any baby who gets little personal attention
> for six months can appear retarded.*

These babies, too young to think or speak, were not too
young to *feel,* not too young to know that they were unloved. Without love, they have no security, no faith in life,
no self-respect, and therefore no respect from others and
no hope of achievement. For these needs—the need for love,

*Trombley, William, "Babies Without Homes," *Saturday Evening Post,*
February 16, 1963, Vol. 236, No. 6, p. 16.

for security and faith, for independence and respect and achievement—all must be satisfied if the individual is to reach his potential.

When a child is relegated to an institution, where little or no effort is made to help him develop his own personality or his abilities, there is a loss not only to the child but through him to his family and so to mankind. Even if he is not placed in an institution until ten years or older, the initial experience of caring for him, of understanding his handicap, of devising ways of helping him to overcome them insofar as possible, and above all, perhaps, the opportunity to love him bring perception and depth to his parents and their other children. They live with and through the situation, instead of relegating and avoiding it, and in the process, life is enriched for them all.

Something like this—but on a far wider scale—occurs in a community when it recognizes that its handicapped citizens, among them the retarded, have a right to respect and affection. When such responsibility has been assumed in a community, usually first through some concerned individual, remarkable results have come about in benefits for so-called "normal" individuals. Such concepts are not new, for mental retardation is not new. More than fifteen centuries before Christ there is mention of mental retardation in the Therapeutic Papyrus of Thebes.* The Greeks knew of mental retardation, but they abandoned children so afflicted, or killed them, and the Romans used them as fools

* "A Historical Survey of Research and Management of Mental Retardation in the United States," by Eugene E. Doll (pamphlet reprinted from *Readings on the Exceptional Child* by E. Philip Trapp and Philip Himelstein, Appleton-Century-Crofts, New York, 1962).

for amusement. The Zoroastrians of Persia, however, gave them tender care. Christianity, too, treated them with compassion, until as the Dark Ages came on they were persecuted as witches. Some effort was made in Gheel, in Brabant, to give them family care, and the United States later followed this example. In England in the Middle Ages they were made wards of the King, but the Reformation brought harsh treatment again. Among the public charges sold into service in New England there were undoubtedly some who were mentally retarded.

Not until the end of the eighteenth century did the concept of training the mentally retarded come into being. Like most discoveries, the idea was expressed through the efforts of an individual, Dr. Jean Marc Gaspard Itard, Chief Medical Officer of the National Institution for the Deaf and Dumb in France, who became concerned about the physical and emotional needs of a boy of about twelve who had been found by some sportsmen as he was roaming naked through the woods, feeding like an animal on acorns and nuts. Victor, as he was later called, though unable to hear loud noises, could hear the fall of a small object. Itard's friends agreed, when this was discovered, that both Victor's sight and touch were defective, and that he was unable to learn because of being severely retarded.

Itard understood the emotional and physical needs of deaf-mutes, for he had worked with them for years, and he was deeply touched by Victor's condition. He longed to help the lad. Apart from his sympathy for the child, Itard believed that Victor could be taught to communicate if someone were sufficiently patient and willing to take the time to teach him. Although severely criticized by his associates, he began his arduous task. Victor learned to distinguish colors and to connect an object with its name, and gradually he developed a close affinity for his governess because his need for attention and love had been partially satisfied.

Finally, much to the astonishment of Itard's critics, Victor learned to read a little. Itard, however, became discouraged and disappointed when he realized that despite all his efforts Victor would never be able to speak, and at last he considered his efforts a complete failure. His associates at the French Academy did not agree, for Itard's teaching of this one retarded child proved for the first time that mentally retarded persons are capable of varying degrees of training. Far more important, his unexpected achievement showed that when, as in this particular case, a person does not learn well the cause may be directly due to a physical defect.

Itard proved, too, that even an imbecile is educable to some degree. By a system of rewards he showed the possibility of using natural desires and needs for educational goals, a principle as sound for the normal individual as for the retarded. In so doing, he also created new desires and to that extent created the possibility of still further development. He based his program on the child's organic needs and thereby devised and put into practice a technique of functional education for life. It was the first scientific treatment of mental retardation.

Twenty years later Belhomme taught severely retarded children in Paris and found that while diagnosis was primary and must precede all else, diagnosis must include inclinations and propensities, a fact as important for the teaching of the normal mind as for the retarded.

The next important name in the training and education of the retarded is that of Édouard Seguin whose work with the retarded led directly to his great influence upon education as a whole. At the suggestion of Itard, Seguin began to teach severely retarded children in a private school in Paris. Later, as a political refugee, he came to the United States and opened a private school in Massachusetts. Other schools were opened in rapid succession, all of them as training schools for education and release of the retarded instead of for custodial care. The goal was the comprehensive harmonious training of the whole child, physically, intellectually and morally. Thus again the teaching of retarded children provided the ideals and methods later used for teaching normal children. In fact, the tempo necessary for teaching children with minds slower than the average allowed time to observe ways in which learning is acquired and upon which the techniques of teaching should be based, exactly as a film in slow motion reveals what takes place in a developing action.

Édouard Seguin never received the recognition he deserved for his influence upon education. Four private training schools were opened in the United States, and Seguin, settling here, was active in all these schools, later establishing his own private school in New York City. These schools were conducted in spite of public disapproval. People could not believe that idiots could be trained, or indeed that it was worthwhile to do so. Yet aside from the humane aspect a respect for these persons as innocent human beings, Seguin was able to say in 1866 that approximately a third of the severely retarded children under his care had been taught good behavior and were working with about a third of normal efficiency. More than 40 percent could carry on the ordinary affairs of life under friendly supervision, with about two-thirds normal efficiency; some 20 to 30 percent came still nearer to the standards of a full man; and the remainder would be difficult to distinguish from normal persons.

Seguin believed in functional education, a very modern conception, new in his day, at which he arrived through his work with retarded children. His technique was the orderly procedure from passive to active, from the known to the unknown, from sensation to perception, from pattern to the spontaneous. He believed in teaching through the activities and materials of everyday life. He believed that the day should begin and end with something pleasant. He emphasized group play, and he made love the basis for all effort.

As one of the first pioneers in service to the retarded, with a sensitivity far beyond that of many of his associates, Seguin's efforts influenced our modern educational practices and theories. He could never prove, as he had hoped, that retardation could be cured but his patient attempts to stir and awaken dormant mental capacities inspired friends and students alike, among whom was Maria Montessori.

This leader stressed the importance of sensory and motor abilities now considered a basic part of today's Special Education. Each humanitarian tried to vary previously accepted methods to improve the lives of retarded children. Not all produced the desired effect, but some exciting results showed that children given training were benefited, and that no service to mankind is unimportant.

The names of Itard, Seguin, Montessori and many others are forgotten by all save a few, but their principles increasingly influence the education of children, normal and retarded.

CHAPTER II

EARLY DISCOVERIES ABOUT
MENTAL ABILITIES

The founder of modern methods for testing and determining intelligence was Alfred Binet. In 1904 the French Government appointed a commission to devise ways of educating retarded children. Its members decided that while the retarded should not attend schools for normal children, they should be given medical and educational examinations before entering special classes. At that time, much confusion existed about the way in which backward children could be identified. Physicians could not agree on their diagnosis of retardation. Apart from being unable to detect whether it was an inherited or acquired condition, they disagreed concerning its extent. Some doctors emphasized noticeable differences in the responses of retarded as opposed to those of normal children. A few placed greater importance on differences in specific physical movements. Others paid more attention to the exaggerated appetite of a child or perhaps to a pronounced speech defect. Educators found it equally difficult to compare the abilities of their pupils. They, too, used different terms when speaking of a retarded child.

These differences interested Binet. What did teachers mean, for example, when they said: "There is a gleam of intelligence in this boy," or "The intellectual faculties of this girl exist in a very incomplete degree"? What was the difference, if any, when they said: "This child has defective speech," as compared to "This person has limited language ability"? Both children who stammer slightly and those whose speech is scarcely intelligible have "defective speech," but Binet knew that such disabilities do not necessarily mean that a person is retarded.

For that matter, how could it be determined whether a child enrolled in a special class for several years had benefited from attendance? After a little girl had been in a hospital or institution for five or six years, how could a doctor decide whether she should be returned to her home? Upon investigation, Binet found that the only method the doctors used was to compare her certificate of entrance with her certificate of dismissal. But, as this psychologist pointed out to his friends, if the two certificates were prepared by different physicians who did not judge the child in the same fashion or who used different words to describe the mental ability of the girl, how could one be assured that she had profited by her hospitalization? Again, without some means of measurement, even if the same person examined the child both when she entered and left the hospital, how could he be certain that his own impressions had not altered?

Binet was aware that with practice and medical insight many physicians and teachers could judge or classify a child, but he also recognized that these judgments could be affected by their own emotions. Obviously, there were two lacks: first, a common denominator for determining individual differences in mentality; and second, mutual agreement between physicians and educators on an acceptable method for measuring these differences. In order to furnish a guide for members of commissions charged with similar responsibilities, therefore, Binet, together with Théodore Simon, began an extended study of both retarded and normal children. First at Salpetrière, and afterward in the primary school of Paris, they prepared a series of very simple tasks which, starting from the lowest intellectual level to that of average normal intelligence, would indicate a child's performance level. The fact that many of these children could not read did not affect their scores.

Binet decided that he would not give them anything to read, anything to write, or anything which would permit an opportunity to succeed by means of rote learning. His only objective was to determine the ability of a child to cope with his own problems.

It was not long before the two investigators discovered that the most important factor in determining intelligence was the ability of a child to adapt to his personal needs and circumstances. To comprehend and to judge well—this, they learned, was the secret. It became apparent that partial or total loss of the use of one or more sense organs did not cause mental retardation. This we now understand. For example, Helen Keller's blindness and deafness postponed but did not prevent her from learning once she was given suitable and patient training. Why? Because her judgment was not affected by her serious physical lacks.

Along these same lines, quite by surprise, it was learned that memory is the grand imitator of intelligence. One retarded girl whom they tested developed a phenomenal memory but she seriously lacked common sense. The reverse they also found to be true. From knowledge such as this, Binet devised a set of thirty tests, the most simple of which determined whether a child could coordinate the movement of his head and eyes in order to see. Each test corresponded to a different level of ability. Since he wished to learn how well a child would think when he became an adult, the last test of Binet's entire group dealt with abstract reasoning. He hoped that from the child's performance would emerge the group of tests needed to obtain a picture of his general intelligence. Throughout his work, Binet intuitively assumed that it made little difference what sort of tasks he used, provided that each task would measure in some way the child's general ability. This assumption explains in part the large variety of tests he employed, and it also accounts for the fact that certain types of items found useful for one age group were not always used at other age levels. From our present knowledge of individual abilities, even more impressive was the fact that the use of a variety of tests to obtain a single measurement produced a much clearer understanding of each child's ability than otherwise could be possible.

"One test signifies nothing, let us emphatically repeat," Binet told his colleagues, "but five or six tests signify something. And this is so true that one might almost say,

'It matters very little what the tests are so long as they are numerous.' " *

Although familiar with and appreciative of the many problems with which parents of retarded children are faced, this far-seeing psychologist was particularly interested in helping teachers. He wanted them to think first in terms of each individual child's needs.

To find out just what instructors of primary grades thought of their own ability to judge children's needs, Binet prepared a simple questionnaire which he asked them to complete in writing. The two questions he asked were: "How many times do you think you have made a mistake in judging a pupil's ability?" and "What method did you use in making your judgment?" Their replies did not surprise him. Some were eight or ten pages in length. What amused him most was that in each case the teacher believed his original idea of the child was the right one and that at no time had he ever been deceived. Binet's scale proved how little we can judge another person's ability without the help of testing procedures.

"We are far from flattering ourselves that we have inaugurated a reform," Binet said when speaking about the scale for determining intelligence which they eventually prepared. "Reforms in France do not succeed except through politics, and we cannot readily imagine a secretary of state busying himself with a question of this kind. What is taught to children at school! As though legislators could become interested in that! . . . Without doubt one could

* Alfred Binet, Sc.D., and Th. Simon, M.D., *The Development of Intelligence in Children* (Vineland: The Training School at Vineland, Translated by Elizabeth S. Kite, 1916), p. 329.

conceive many possible applications of the process, in dreaming of a future where the social sphere would be better organized than ours; where every one would work according to his known aptitudes in such a way that no particle of psychic force should be lost for society. That would be the ideal city. It is indeed far from us." *

Binet thought he was dreaming. What would he say now were he to know that in a country such as ours President Kennedy had personally initiated a nationwide program to provide for the needs of all retarded persons, and that President Johnson has continued the comprehensive program plan to combat retardation. How far we have come in society since Binet began applying his ability to the needs of others! In those days, however, news traveled slowly. Some time passed before the results of his remarkable study reached America. And, unfortunately, it received very little attention. In 1906, however, when the Vineland Research Laboratory of the Training School at Vineland, New Jersey, was opened, its director, Dr. Henry H. Goddard, began seeking information to assist him in his own work with retarded children. Two years later while in Europe, he learned about Binet's tests. He was a person who was willing to try a new idea in spite of being dubious about its value, and upon his return to this country he began to use the tests with children at the Training School. To his delight, he found that the procedure met his needs.

In 1909, when a revision of the original tests was published in the now well-known form, The Binet Measuring Scale of Intelligence, Goddard said: "Probably no critic . . . reacted against it more positively than did I at the

* *Ibid.*, p. 262.

first reading. It seemed impossible to grade intelligence in that way. It was too easy, too simple." *

Simple? Yes, but are not the greatest discoveries those which appear simple after their complexity has been made plain to us by a genius? The following year, to assist other American psychologists, Dr. Goddard prepared and published a brief outline of the original Binet-Simon article explaining the use of the Scale. Later, permission was obtained to publish a literal translation, the demand for which became so great that by 1916 the Vineland Laboratory alone, without any effort to advertise its use, had upon request distributed 22,000 copies in addition to 88,000 of the record blanks to be used when conducting the test. By this time Binet's contribution to society was receiving worldwide attention, for translations of the Scale had been distributed in fifteen countries. Its impact was revolutionary, and yet, as with all new ideas, out of every nook and cranny came the critics. They could not understand the Scale and so they would not accept it.

It is likely that a few psychologists felt that although Binet gave credit for the correctness of a child's response, since this frequently depends upon the ability of the child to manipulate words or objects rather than upon his understanding of their meaning, it placed far too much emphasis on language. They questioned its validity in regard to speed. Though these criticisms were often exaggerated, they did contain some value. The average boy or girl will generally respond when asked to say as many words as he can think of in three minutes, or make a sen-

* *Ibid.,* p. 5.

tence out of a jumble of selected words, but how can one be certain that he knows their significance?

Those who had never attempted to devise a test may have cried, "No wonder he developed one for children— they are always available in school. It only goes as far as age fifteen; what good would it be for adults?" It was, however, difficult for them to dismiss it from their minds. If the method had merit, a few men began to wonder whether they could prepare something similar for adults, something which could help in the selection of employ- ment best suited to individual capabilities. This, they realized, would have to be a test designed specifically for older people, a test for which speed would be but one of several measures of ability.

Since certain of Binet's questions did not apply to Ameri- can children, changes in his original test were considered, of which the Stanford Revision of the Binet-Simon Test is one of the best known and widely used. Soon open-minded persons, willing and eager to try these tests, learned that a well-trained psychologist after an hour of testing could more accurately tell the difference between superior, aver- age, and dull children than a teacher who had been observ- ing the same children over a period of several months. As people became better acquainted with the questions and realized the ease with which the tests could be given and their effectiveness with both normal and retarded children, they agreed that although originally standardized on chil- dren, the Scale could be extended and improved for use with all ages.

These tests offered a new basis for *classifying degrees of retardation.* Psychologists no longer needed to speak of "social defectives" or "moral imbeciles." They began talking in terms of a fifteen-year-old whose individual mental age was that of a ten-year-old child. For the first time in history a retarded child was thought of as one who, though he might lack the ability even to care for his own needs, was nevertheless a person who might be helped to use the ability he had. This test, and others which have been devised since then, formed the basis for determining mental functioning.

CHAPTER III

VISTAS OF UNDERSTANDING

During this early period of special work with and for children, very few adults were tested except those in prison and in mental hospitals. It was not until 1917, when the U. S. Army enlisted the help of psychologists for the purpose of classifying soldiers, that many of these individual tests were tried out on a large scale with normal adults. To meet the need of such numbers, however, and because of the urgency of examining them quickly in a relatively short time, use of the Stanford Revision was found to be impracticable. Psychologists then devised the now famous Army Alpha and Beta group tests.

As Binet had emphasized over and over again, results of even one or two individual tests do not always give a correct picture of a person's true ability. One soldier during World War II failed three tests because his mental age was considered less than that of a child of eight. Upon examination, however, it was found that he had been earning $75 a week as a skilled oil driller before being inducted into the army. He had supported his entire family for years, and yet was being considered unfit for duty!

This classic example showed that in addition to measures of intelligence other tests were needed to compare general knowledge, individual preferences and abilities for specific vocations. Thus psychologists and educators, interested in testing procedures, began devoting a large part of their energies to the development of new tests for the mentally retarded. Since preschool children have a limited vocabulary and often refuse to cooperate unless given interesting materials, simple performance tests were developed. From these, examiners were able to discover whether a child could put blocks together or arrange an object in its proper form as quickly as another child of the same age. Additional tests were devised to determine a child's powers of recognition, discrimination, and coordination. From the results, schedules were prepared for different age levels. Up to that time we knew little about a child's mental ability until he was old enough to be enrolled in school.

As these new varieties of tests became readily available and were used more and more with retarded and normal children, individual differences became clearer. Previously we had thought of reading as a relatively simple skill; quite to the contrary, it was found to be most complex. School children with reading problems were found to be having difficulty not only with spelling but with arithmetic as well.

One little girl did not seem to have the ability to form an association between the sound and meaning of the words she was reading and so was failing in several subjects. However, when the teacher read arithmetic problems aloud to the child she gave all the correct answers. Later when given the same problems to read, she could not get any of them right. It was because she could not read well, *not* that she did not understand or comprehend arithmetic. This is similar to those whose hearing deficiency makes it difficult to associate subjects with the printed word.

Such discoveries finally led to the development of our present-day emphasis on remedial reading, which within the past decade has prevented so many children from school failure. Test results showed that because of individual differences, our methods of instruction must be adapted to the needs of each child. Repetitious spelling drills, necessary for retarded children, were found to be unnecessary for those with superior mentality. For the first time it was recognized not only that a gifted child is unwilling to spend time drilling on the same word but that he often makes errors because he spells the word as it sounds in an attempt to generalize from past experience.

At no period in history had there been a lack of recognition of high intelligence, but outstanding accomplishments were usually not evident until adolescence, and sometimes not until late adulthood. Intelligence tests indicated the existence of more children with better than average performance than might have been expected in relation to the number of famous men and women in the history of the world.

Doors of knowledge began opening which revealed, too, a direct connection between physical handicaps and learning ability. Throughout the years many handicapped but mentally normal children struggled with their classwork with little success and, subjected to failure, were later considered retarded. Psychological tests showed that in addition to specialized medical services, these children required individualized educational services, with a much slower introduction to new and more difficult materials.

"My son can't make his hand do what his mind commands. He knows what he wants to write, but he can't make the pencil obey," was a frequently heard explanation from the mother of a cerebral-palsied child.

To assist these children, the importance and relationship of normal intelligence to the special characteristics and particular physical needs of each child were made a matter of study. Medical evaluations revealed that apart from well-known chronic defects and orthopedic conditions, the interference to learning could be caused by as relatively easy a thing to prevent as, for example, tooth decay. Some tests showed the influence of opinions and attitudes of other persons upon the learning ability and emotional growth of a handicapped person. Such an influence, we now understand, can create far more limitation than any imposed by a physical defect.

The impressive range of measures for testing abilities of both normal and retarded persons, however, still included a major lack. Although by 1933 one published list gave the names of 4,000 different tests, we still could not compare our own behavior with that of other persons. Perhaps of all tests this was the most difficult to devise, because it involves conduct. Intelligence tests provided information about how well a person understands and is able to solve simple and abstract problems. Aptitude tests indicated individual differences in mechanical, musical, and other areas. But the underlying question as to the cause of our actions remained an enigma.

What do we really mean when we say a person is "mature" and yet label another "immature"? We inherit a brain but behavior patterns are learned. It is the same with fear. We learn to be afraid of people or things, or we learn to have confidence in others. But why? It is because we learn to adapt to situations differently. We do not just act, we act in accordance with our individual natures and personalities. Though they may change, they will remain slightly different from someone else's. It is a matter of individuality—certainly not a matter of intelligence.

Binet had emphasized that no two children fulfill their needs in exactly the same manner. He spoke of these differences in terms of one child's being more able to adapt to life than another. A few, for example, may be quite persuasive with parents and friends, while others obtain the same result by being domineering.

Following a regular weekly staff conference about patients who were being considered for home placement, the superintendent of an institution and one of his doctors began discussing their ability to judge each case. "I know you believe Marie Dubinsky is ready to go home," said the psychiatrist to his employer, "but I firmly disagree. What makes you think she can adapt to her family when even here in this atmosphere she acts like a child?"

"Perhaps you're right. I realize she doesn't care for herself at the table, but at least she is quiet—that's much better than when she arrived. But how much better? To what degree has she improved? You've been giving her therapy treatments. Frankly, we don't have a test we can give to such people—it's all still a matter of our subjective feelings."

We can present a normal child with a series of arithmetic problems and by his success in solving them measure his ability in this subject. But what about his personality? With a preschool child what causes one to cry, cling to his mother, refuse to try the tests and object to remaining in the room, whereas another will attempt to take over the examination by refusing to remain seated and constantly run around or perform acrobatics? It is impossible to take a person apart as one does a watch, and yet, if in school a boy continues to lie or steal, we always want to know the underlying cause for his behavior. How else can we help him?

How mature are we—in our reactions to others? When receiving a compliment do we accept it in the kind manner in which it was meant or in every case do we immediately wonder if it was given for an ulterior motive? We do not question why an emotionally disturbed child is afraid of strangers, but many normal persons react in a similar fashion. Let us take it a step further. Is one man more mature than his brother because he has chosen to spend his life in a small office or work in an institution, because he wants, he says, "to serve others"? Or, is someone else the more mature because he chooses to think only of himself and his immediate family, remaining in an untenable employment situation for years because the salary is good?

As men are challenged by their own lack of knowledge, and as Itard had been emotionally challenged by one child, so educators and psychologists were continually challenged by differences in the behavior of retarded children of the same age at the Training School in Vineland, New Jersey. Why, for example, was one boy willing to feed and dress himself, but another unwilling even to try to supply his own needs?

Distracted teachers wondered whether a test could be developed which would be based on the presence or absence of certain everyday common activities or behavior characteristics of say, one-year-old children, then two, three, and so on—right up to those persons we consider mature adults.

They found that with little tots, if they wished to learn when the children started to stand alone or to follow simple instructions, it was necessary to question their parents.

From this germ of an idea, Edgar A. Doll, the Director of Research at Vineland, began the slow process of selecting a list of questions that could be used to compare the ability of normal and retarded children to supply their own personal needs, and, as they matured, to supply the needs of others. Beginning with eighteen separate questions relating to babies from birth to the age of one year, and so on for each successive year to the age of twenty-five, a total of 117 separate items were prepared and grouped according to each level. For example, the simplest of these included such questions as: "At what month did your child learn to grasp an object within reach?" "At what time in his life was he able to sit unsupported?" and "How old was he when he first drank from a cup or glass without help?" Each category involved ordinary activities of daily living, beginning with problems of general self-help on through more difficult ones, including the ability of a person to travel alone, to purchase clothing for himself, and finally, to perform expert or professional work for himself as well as for others in the community.

No test previously devised had afforded such an excellent measure of the individual's ability to care for himself. The Vineland Social Maturity Scale, as it was named when published almost twenty years ago, has enabled us, for example, to determine the best type of home into which an orphan should be placed. The results of this Scale help us to determine whether a retarded or emotionally disturbed child should be sent to an institution. Its adaptation for blind preschool children has been proved effective. It gives clues as to the tendencies of juvenile delinquency, and has therefore been a means of preventing more serious problems. It helps to identify mentally normal persons suffering from emotional maladjustments, those whose abilities are slowly regressing because of a mental or physical handicap, and provides information about individual differences in personality which specifically identify epileptic and psychopathic behavior. More impressive, this test is still as helpful as when first used. It can even measure improvement in a person's behavior while he is receiving special treatment, therapy, or training.

Even though a child may have made a poor score on an intelligence test, his grade on the Vineland Scale may indicate that with proper help he will be able to adjust to his own needs at home. Indeed, this measurement of ability, in addition to others, has afforded a guide for improved living for everyone. It has helped us discover when and how much individuals are able to learn, what they can do, and how they may best fulfill the purpose of their lives.

Teachers no longer need blindly enroll a child in the

first grade and then find to their disappointment that he cannot learn. Preschool tests are given today to a child to supply us with objective reasons why he may or may not be able to benefit from training. It need not be entirely guesswork as to whether a boy has mechanical ability or an exceptional aptitude for science. We have tests to help us determine his interests and abilities. Tests will assist in determining whether a girl who wishes to become a nurse will be able to withstand, both emotionally and mentally, the rigorous three-year hospital course required to wear the honored nurse's cap.

Now, when we speak of classifying intelligence, our classification does not correspond to the chemist's arrangement of elements or the zoologist's subdivision of animals into vertebrates and invertebrates. Instead, we liken intelligence to the colors of the rainbow—an uninterrupted spectrum of light flowing from orange-yellow into yellow and from indigo into deep violet. One level of intelligence merges into the next. At one end of our rainbow are those who will never be able to supply their needs. These we call "severely retarded." Next are those who, with help, can take care of many of their own needs, the "trainable retarded." Still others are the "educable retarded," who, when given special training, can become useful, employable citizens. Then comes the great majority of normal persons, and so on until we reach the far end of the rainbow of intellect, where we find those we call gifted, superior on the level of genius.

Our way of life is now a psychological test-oriented one. It would be difficult to find a child in school or an adult at work who has not been given several different kinds of such tests. From the assembly line operator or filing clerk to our top executives, there is scarcely anyone for whom some kind of skillful testing technique has not been devised to assist in determining his ability for employment, job assignment, transfer, or promotion.

As each grain of sand differs from another, so these tests indicate how we differ as individuals, but like the sands of the sea, there must also be a fundamental basis of unity, a large degree of like-mindedness. Where can such unity be found among persons of widely divergent personalities? This like-mindedness can be found only in an element of equal measure, regardless of intelligence or ability. One common bond of unity, for example, can be found in the realm of ideals, for the moving power of ideals is connected not so much with intelligence as with emotions. The vast majority of our population is distinctly capable of absorbing, accepting, and living up to our American ideals and way of life. It is we who must make it possible for each person to contribute his share.

What man does *not* know he can neither act upon nor fear. What man *does* know will largely control his behavior. If he is told that the world is flat, he will sail his ships to a point and no farther. If he is told that in a far country men have discovered yellow sand, he will drop his way of life and rush for gold. When he is told that he can reach the moon he will bend every effort to get there. If he is told that some people are his friends and others are his enemies, he will like and dislike accordingly. The way our world is imagined and the manner in which we form our goals and opinions will determine what each citizen can do for himself and his country.

Such men as Binet and Doll are our benefactors. Binet humbly described his own efforts as a "rough sketch of a work which was directly inspired by the desire to serve the interesting cause of the education of subnormals." * Instead, his inspiration gave us a tool of knowledge. As he so ably declared when concluding his first report: "We have only wished to prove that it is possible to find in a precise and truly scientific way, the level of intelligence, to compare that level with a normal level, and consequently to conclude how many years a child is retarded. In spite of the inevitable errors of an initial work, which is mere groping, we believe we have made our demonstration."

Now we know that the precise, careful use of his testing procedures have provided society with a new way in which to solve the problems of mankind. It has helped us to understand ourselves. It has given us a deeper appreciation of the needs of those we cherish. From it we are continuing to discover how to live happier, more useful lives and how best to serve our fellowmen. This gift, indirectly given by a Parisian to retarded boys and girls, is still teaching all of us lessons in the art of living.

* Binet: *Op. cit.*, p. 9.

CHAPTER IV

SEEKING NEW TRUTHS

We live in an exciting period of man's history. It is an astronautical age and an electronic era. The generation of which we are a part is also one of microscopic and genetic advancement.

Throughout the ages, man has always believed that nature fixes certain limits on his achievements. For this reason, each succeeding generation has declared its goals and has also set specific boundaries to what it deemed possible for accomplishment. Certain limitations were accepted without question; others man attempted to conquer. But as man's knowledge slowly increased, a later generation made up its mind to assault previously assumed impossibilities. The differing assessment of what seems practical, as compared to what appears to be forbidden by circumstances beyond control, has distinguished or been the means of comparing individual periods of man's development.

One need only mention the Stone Age for a lad in the

eighth grade to have a clear mental picture of a husky person seated on the ground slowly and painstakingly chiseling a rock into the form of an implement to make life easier. Our photographic memory skims along to reproduce a panorama of paintings depicting the changes which came into the lives of millions during the Industrial Age. Our forefathers saw the harnessing of electricity. We have watched with awe the smashing of the atom into its minute particles. It has been, and still is, a fantastic progression and expansion of man's ability to control the elements of nature which wait in silence either to be combined or to be broken apart in order that their power may be released.

Today we proudly proclaim this the Space Age. Our youth speak in terms of light years as we once spoke of a century. It is, however, quite conceivable that historians may consider our era in time, this brief section of eternity, the Medical Age. If so, they will be accurate. Their description of events could very well be based on the astounding control we have achieved in relation to our own bodily functions, the knowledge we have acquired about the development of the human brain, and man's extended longevity, which has been provided by the use of new drugs. Far more important, they would stress our ever-increasing awareness of specific disabilities such as mental retardation, for which medical science has offered so little hope of cure. Prevention or alleviation has now become our ultimate goal!

During the past fifty years, more has been discovered about the human organism than ever before in the entire history of the world. We need no longer slowly but inevitably destroy ourselves with tuberculosis, for example.

Our X-ray teams tour the country so that periodically we may be assured that our bodies are free of devastating tuberculosis germs. As a result, within the past five years tuberculosis has been reduced here in the United States by 30 percent.

Even a seemingly bizarre idea, running contrary to so-called "common sense," when objectively studied has sometimes removed barriers of ignorance. As a result of the unexpected recovery of seriously wounded soldiers following surgery performed near the battle lines during World War II, our entire postoperative treatment of patients has been altered. Even as late as 1930, such persons would have been forced to lie in a hospital bed for ten days or more. Now they are directed to get up and move about within hours.

Formerly ill-considered but imaginative ideas recently put into action by biological scientists and laboratory technicians have also been the means of developing amazing methods of treatment and prevention of illness. A classic example is the widespread impact made upon infectious diseases by penicillin and sulfa drugs. Equally revolutionary in its effect is the vaccine against measles. This disease, if followed by encephalitis, can cause serious disability. At the turn of this century these preventive measures would have been unbelievable to practicing physicians.

The process of learning how to prevent disease is expensive. It involves not only the time and talent of many specialists but also the cooperation of hundreds of patients. As with any experimentation, throughout the often prolonged process some findings prove negative. Though seldom of interest to the public, these data are still very useful in the step-by-step procedure taken by scientists when attempting to solve a human problem. If it concerns the general public eventually we may hear the names of those who are responsible for the research project, but it is a rare circumstance if we ever learn about the countless other persons who made possible the final result. For example, how many men and women fully recognize the part mentally retarded persons both in public and private schools and hospitals have played in the development of preventive medicine?

Seldom have the results of medical research been given such worldwide publicity as the unraveling of the clinical mystery presented by poliomyelitis. The development by Enders of culture techniques to prevent the effect of the polio virus, which later contributed to the long-desired and now widely administered Salk vaccine, we still consider a miracle. Now has come the final miracle of an oral preventive developed by Sabin. The effect of all this on our own lives and those of millions of unborn babies can never be estimated. Yet of all the hundreds of thousands of persons who have benefited by its powerful action, few realize that Dr. Jonas Salk studied the immunizing properties of this vaccine on retarded patients at the Polk State School and Hospital in Pennsylvania!

Prior to the time he went to Polk, Dr. Salk was certain that the vaccine was safe. He had given it to himself, his family and a few other patients but he needed more evidence of its effectiveness. In cooperation with the staff, selected patients were chosen for possible experimentation none of whom, however, participated in the research without the written permission of their parents. Today, in testimony to their contribution there hangs in the office of the superintendent a bronze plaque on which are these words: "The Leo E. Sattler Memorial Award presented to the children of Polk State School commemorating the service they rendered to humanity in the development of the Salk Polio Vaccine, November 11, 1952."

Yes, the use of retarded children in several outstanding medically oriented projects has been a major factor in altering our American way of life and will affect the future destiny of millions throughout the world. It may even be said that the part retarded children have played in the development of our medical and biological achievements has helped to improve our present national standard of health.

Within the past two decades, formidable sums have been poured into research by both public and private agencies. The National Institute of Neurological Diseases and Blindness alone has spent more than eleven million dollars, about one-fourth of its fiscal 1962 research appropriation, to support 151 projects aimed at increasing our knowledge of the causes, prevention, and treatment of mental retardation and retarded disorders. The Institute's major research endeavor, the Collaborative Perinatal Research Project, which has been in operation for over six years, has as its primary goal the discovery of clues to the causes of mental retardation, cerebral palsy, and kindred disorders. This one project eventually will involve examination from early pregnancy through labor and delivery of some fifty thousand expectant mothers, and a review of their children from birth to school age. In his speech to the 88th Congress, the late President Kennedy gave the highest priority to prevention of mental illness and mental retardation, and now it seems probable that even greater sums will be allotted by state and federal legislators to this one facet of our national budget.

Research teams, working either in university or medical settings, have an occupational language of their own. Scientists speak in their own special terms just as hardware salesmen identify the price of an item in their triple-sized catalogue by a set of numerical codes. When they discuss the thousands of things they sell, expressions and phrases which are familiar to them may sound confusing to the average consumer, like the prescription which the doctor instructs us to take to a pharmacist. The information on the little slip of paper can readily be deciphered by the druggist, but to us it looks like a foreign language. It is the same with many reports prepared by research specialists. To appreciate their value, we must have their meanings translated into layman's language.

Thus, in order to rouse us from our national complacency and to give us a better understanding of the need for more research, the President's Panel on Mental Retardation has had to be specific. Some people still consider the phrase "mental retardation" synonymous with "mental illness." In reality, a mentally retarded person is one who has either incomplete or impaired mental development. A delay in—or lack of—mental growth may be due to one or a combination of reasons. Dr. George Tarjan, vice-chairman of the Panel and head of one of the California state schools for the retarded, says that there are at least seventy known different causes for mental retardation. These may occur before birth, during birth, or in childhood. For example, specific glandular disorders, an irregular development of the genes of either parent, or chemical poisons during pregnancy may cause retardation of an unborn baby. An incorrect position of the child before birth or a difficult delivery can be a factor. Many conditions after birth, such as the inability of the body to assimilate protein properly or an inflammation of the brain caused by meningitis, may result in delayed mental maturity or the complete inability of a child's mind to mature.

Diagnosing mental retardation is a difficult and highly technical task. We judge a child's physical growth with a scale or yardstick, but how do we determine his mental development? Very few retarded children show such clear evidence of retardation at birth or soon after as to leave little doubt about their mental condition. The great majority lack any physical sign of delayed mental growth. Thus, to judge their ability we must compare their growth and progress with that of normal children of the same age. For instance, did it take longer for one child to start to hold things, to recognize people and simple objects? No matter what may be the cause of retardation, if when given several tasks a child can only achieve about three-fourths as much as normal children of his age, he may be considered as having an IQ of about 75. Unfortunately, an IQ merely gives us an overall average of a person's ability. No one single measure is adequate.

In difficult cases, only a diagnosis and evaluation resulting from the joint study of a pediatrician, neurologist, psychiatrist, psychologist, social worker, and often other professional staff can be considered satisfactory. According to the severity of the problem the emphasis varies. Experience, however, has shown that almost all persons with an

IQ of below 70 have difficulty in adapting to life. Approximately 5.4 million of our present population may be considered in this group. Since 126,000 retarded children are born each year, it is estimated that by 1970 there will be one million more persons in the United States in this category unless major advances are made in the prevention of retardation. Fortunately, of this appalling number only a very small percentage requires constant supervision. From these figures it becomes apparent that in addition to learning about the incompletely understood causes of retardation, more emphasis must be placed on adequate prenatal and obstetric care, immunization, and health supervision of young children—an increased parent and community education. This in itself is of value, too, for the normal child.

Many basic sciences have coordinated their efforts to provide the information now available. Of the projects currently being supported by the U. S. Department of Health, Education, and Welfare, more than half the total number are studies of a psychological and educational nature. Of these, a great many have been devoted to research in the behavioral sciences. In each area of investigation there is a tremendous diversity both as to the nature and the type of group being studied. It is all aimed, however, toward remediation, education, and habilitation of retarded persons. Projects range from the evaluation of various aspects of educational programs to studies of ways to compare brain-injured children with those who are retarded due to other causes, and include studies in epidemiology, therapy, hearing difficulties, speech loss, and many others.

It would be impossible to rank the recent achievements

of any one group either separately or jointly. Each has been dramatic in its own right. Neither is it practical to attempt even a summary of the many successful projects which have been supported wholly, or in part, by federal, state, or private funds since this information is available upon request. All, however, have a direct effect on future generations. Our expanded understanding of human chromosomes is an excellent example. Let us take the experience of an air pilot as he related it to a geneticist:

"My wife and I had studied biology in school," he explained. "We knew something about Mendel's laws as they applied to heredity, but it really didn't mean anything to us."

"I'm not surprised," the physician replied. "It has only been within the past few years that his theory was questioned—1956, perhaps. Until about 1956, we all accepted the idea that the normal human number of chromosomes was forty-eight, or twenty-four pairs. Now, through experimentation we've learned the normal number is forty-six."

"Come to think of it, I'd never seen a mongoloid child. Naomi and I were married just before I went overseas and the child was born while I was away. Naturally, I counted the days until I received my orders to go home. Every flight I took while scanning the horizon I wondered what it would be to see my own child. Naomi met me in New York City and we went on a little spree for several days. Her mother took care of the child during our holiday. I guess during those days I was so happy to be with my wife that although there were times when I wondered why she was too quiet, I never suspected.

"When we went home—well, it was hell. I can't describe it. Naomi said she had been to see several physicians and that she was just waiting for me to decide what to do with the child. I blamed her—no one in our family had ever looked like that! Then I blamed myself. We read everything we could get our hands on—what to do and when, but not *why*. That was always how our conversations ended —even when we could talk a little rationally. Finally, one of our neighbors told me that you were going to speak at that meeting and he invited me to go along. Since then, Naomi and I have had a different life."

"A very simple talk," said the weary geneticist. "Sometimes I wonder if these trips are worth the effort, and whether I've been able to explain to people so far removed from my work just what I mean. There is, you know, no cure for mental retardation—prevention, sometimes, but no cure. We know of no way to replace brain cells that have been injured or destroyed or have not developed. In your field, you pilots have the advantage. If a plane disintegrates, you search for debris from which the aircraft manufacturer attempts to determine the cause of the accident. We can't do that. Genes, or units of inheritance, are much, much too small. We infer their presence by the effect they have because they are contained within chromosomes, and these we can only see through a microscope. But we know now why your little daughter is what we call a mongoloid. The normal human number of chromosomes is forty-six, or twenty-three pairs. Mongoloids carry an abnormal forty-seven chromosomes. In the particular one we list as number 'twenty-one,' instead of having but two, a retarded child of this type invariably has three pairs."

Further investigation of this cause for mental retardation indicates that mothers of mongoloid children may be carriers of this same unusual pair of chromosomes. Though mentally normal themselves, these so-called "carriers" can transfer this oddly filled one, number twenty-one, to as high as 50 percent of their children. Fortunately, such hereditary disorders are sporadic and seldom affect others of the same family.

Another example accounting for approximately 1 percent of all retardation is phenylketonuria, commonly known as PKU. It is a metabolic disorder caused by lack of the enzymes in the liver necessary to utilize essential proteins. Without these enzymes the proteins destroy brain cells by strong acids in the blood. Not as an exercise for the mind, but because we wanted to know whether many people understood the value of this one very important discovery, which has been widely publicized, we began asking dozens of people, "What do members of the medical profession mean when they speak of someone having PKU?"

Their replies differed considerably. One woman said, "It has something to do with an overdose of barbiturates." Another answered, "I really don't know, but I believe it is a form of very severe skin rash." One direct reply was, "It relates to the inability of the body to assimilate protein properly." Still another said, "It is an inherited mental deficiency, and has something to do with the enzymes in our bodies. Something goes wrong, like a person having thyroid trouble." Obviously the first two answers to our questions were most inaccurate. They do, however, indicate one thing. Despite an ever-increasing effort to publicize on a nationwide basis any new advance in medical knowledge, there still remains a tragic delay in the understanding of such information by the general public. Gradually however, prevention of mental retardation at least from this cause is taking place. There are children now approaching their teens who were born with phenylketonuria but, thanks to early diagnosis and special diet, have developed normally. It is even possible that in a few years the special diet can be abandoned. The difference between past and present is strikingly illustrated in the case of one family in which there are two girls with phenylketonuria. The older one is severely retarded but the younger, born since the primary research was made, is growing up a normal child. Special credit in the field of phenylketonuria must go to the great Norwegian biochemist, Dr. Afbjorn Fölling.

Not only in the United States but also in England, Norway, Sweden, Denmark, Japan, and many other countries, premarital examination of the parents, early diagnosis of the child, and a faithfully followed phenlalanine-free diet is making possible normal mental development in a large percentage of PKU children. The diet may be necessary only for the critical time in which growth of the brain and nervous system is taking place. Since statistics show that about one in every 200 persons is a carrier of this "irregular chemical trait," if we may call it that, this knowledge of prevention and treatment cannot be overemphasized. As with abnormal genes, even though the "carrier" is not afflicted, marriage of two such persons can produce the disease in about one-quarter of their children. Therefore, across the length and breadth of our nation a movement is on foot to enact state legislation which would require physicians to test babies within the first 72 hours of life, or initiate statewide testing programs for PKU at no cost to hospitals or hospital laboratories. The latter method is preferred by many physicians. The prediction is that this simple, inexpensive and accurate blood test to discover and then correct this one condition leading to mental retardation will constitute a major breakthrough in finding and treating a number of other ailments which cause retardation.

What we have been saying about PKU might just as easily have been said about another similar cause for severe retardation, galactosemia, for which dietary control is also now possible. Though science has not yet been able to alter enzymes within the cell, those outside the cell can be treated, as in the case of the replacement of insulin for diabetes. Progress is even being made in the area of replacing functional molecules. All this gives much promise for the future and proves that hereditary diseases are not therapeutically hopeless. Incredible as it may seem, many experts believe that perhaps one-third of mental retardation, as we now understand it, can be avoided.

Proper prenatal care is often the key to the problem. Statistics show that pregnant women receiving no prenatal care, or prenatal care starting late in pregnancy, have more premature deliveries than those who receive more adequate medical attention. Why in our country do women neglect such service? The first reason relates to the prenatal facilities themselves. There can be many factors including physical absence, economic barriers, inconvenience of location, lack of transportation, and more shocking, sometimes discriminatory practices.

Second, some women do not receive care because of the poor quality of service that is given by those offering it. Third, many women are not sufficiently motivated to make the necessary effort to secure prenatal care. Others are not convinced of its need. Poor motivation is often closely allied with social and economic factors. In such cases good nutrition during nine months of pregnancy cannot make up for twenty years of poor diet. Excellent medical care during that important period cannot fully overcome the harmful effects of a lifetime of poor service. Unfortunately those now most lacking in motivation to obtain help are those most in need. Many of these require intensive maternal and infant care. They are frequently the ones who have poor past obstetrical histories, including previous birth complications, and many of them appear at the hospital's doors already in labor.

To help reduce the incidence of mental retardation caused by complications related to childbearing, Public Law 88-156, the Maternal and Child Health and Mental Retardation Planning Amendments of 1963, provides a new authorization for Special Project Grants for Maternity and Infant Care. Federal funds authorized for this program total $110 million from 1964 through 1968. In the so-called "high risk" groups, both in urban and rural areas, these special funds may be used to pay for professional services and other items of direct cost. Wise use of these funds is one major way we can prevent retardation.

Along these lines we believe that provision should be made for a limited number of government supported prenatal clinics offering superior care both in needed rural and urban locations. Such clinics could provide direct services to those women not now receiving care. They could also serve as models to improve the level of prenatal care provided by other facilities in the area.

For the many yet unborn children who could live normal lives it behooves us to do our part. One very simple thing each of us can do is to provide expectant mothers with the recently published pamplet entitled, "Expectant Mothers: What You Should Know About Mental Retardation: What You Can Do." It is concise and informative and can be obtained from the National Association for Retarded Children.

Advances in medical science have lengthened our life-span. Although we do not know how to restore dead brain cells, science has discovered various surgical and nonsurgical ways to aid a person in the use of those cells which are still functioning normally. Athetoid cerebral-palsied children with mid-brain injuries, adults suffering from the slow degeneration of Parkinson's Disease, those who might have lost eyesight because of a tumor, and many hyperactive persons have been given new lives as a result of neurosurgery. Twenty years ago we had never heard of a brain-injured child getting well. It happens frequently today. Thousands of children have gone back to school after an operation to permit the spinal fluid to move more freely through the body.

Much has been said about the importance of environmental stimulation in mental development. The pure behavioral scientist is apt to say that being reared in a very poor economic environment develops the type of person who is retarded. The neurologist is apt to say the experience of this kind of living, generation after generation, may well develop certain neurological deficits which we cannot, at this point, detect, diagnose or determine. Fully aware of this, President Kennedy's Panel on Mental Retardation recommended that ten research centers be established. Of their 95 major recommendations, this they considered to be one of the most important. Since many disciplines would be involved in joint research endeavors, such centers could provide not only information about the causes of mental retardation but be the means of preventing additional problems now common to normal growth and development.

The normal growth and development of a normal child is a beauty to behold. Abnormal development of any person is heartrending. Through science, we live in an era of hope.

CHAPTER V

EDUCATIONAL ADVANCEMENTS
FOR THE RETARDED

"Laggards!"

"The bane of teachers!"

"Drones who prevent the progress of all other pupils!"

These are but a few of the uncomplimentary remarks used for years to describe overage boys and girls who, after repeating grade after grade, were finally sent home still incapable of contributing their share to society. Many of these so-called "dull, indifferent children," however, have given the world an opportunity to observe democracy in action.

To those who wonder how our society operates and still question whether every human being has potential for useful service, our retarded children have contributed to the development of a national concern for the exceptional needs of *every* person. In capsule form it is democracy at work—an undeniable expression of the American way of life. Interest in the individual, zeal of parents, an open forum for public debate of a problem which cost an estimated 10 percent of public school expenditures, public information resulting in legislation, and finally, the translation of what began as a conviction of a few into a national program. This is the saga of educational programs for the retarded.

When at last we became aware that retarded children were present in large numbers, parents, educators, and psychologists alike turned their attention to the problem of developing learning processes to fit their needs. At the turn of the century it was a rather widespread form of experimentation. Gradually, a distinction became acceptable between those "who could learn to read" whom we called "educable," and those considered "uneducable," with an IQ below 50. By 1920, as a result of modified teaching methods, equipment, and materials, educable children were placed in special learning groups. Though many persons questioned whether the less able were a public school responsibility, they were admitted to some classes if they showed minimal physical or behavioral difficulties and indicated good social adjustment. All other retarded children, however, were until comparatively recently excluded from any type of school life.

It was natural that parents of these untutored, neglected children felt this to be undemocratic both in principle and practice. Educators became acutely aware that parents needed help to train their retarded children in personal hygiene, speech, emotional control, and simple daily tasks. The concern of parents was augmented by the efforts of professionals and in 1950 the National Association for Retarded Children was created. Through its efforts, augmented by local groups of parents, school boards began to realize that financial planning should be diversified, depending on the results obtained from carefully prepared surveys of children who could benefit from individualized attention.

In 1954, the U. S. Office of Education Conference on Qualification and Preparation of Teachers of Exceptional Children accepted a "Creed for Exceptional Children" and the national picture changed. Of tremendous significance were two specific sections:

We Believe that the nation as a whole, every state and county, every city and hamlet, and every citizen, has an obligation to help in bringing to fruition in this generation the ideal of a full and useful life for every exceptional child in accordance with his capacity: the child who is handicapped by defects of speech, of sight, or of hearing, the child whose life may be adversely influenced by a crippling disease or condition, the child whose adjustment to society is made difficult by emotional or mental disorders, and the child who is endowed with special gifts of mind and spirit.

We Believe in the sensitive interpretation of the exceptional child and his needs by teachers and others in order that an attitude favorable to his acceptance and development may be engendered and sustained in the community.*

Within less than a decade every state has passed special legislation and makes some financial contribution to the education of these children. Two hundred fifty thousand

* "Creed for Exceptional Children." Accepted by the U. S. Office of Education Conference on Qualification and Preparation of Teachers of Exceptional Children, October 29, 1954.

of our nation's 1¼ million school-age retarded were enrolled in classes by 1962. Although gravely aware of our existing obligation to all the other retarded boys and girls still waiting to be given the same opportunity for individual development, we can rejoice that instead of doing violence to educational practices, this living, breathing act of a democratic society has hastened recognition of the varying capacities and differing abilities of *all* children.

Far more personalized service is now being provided to homebound pupils than before our retarded children taught us the necessity of individual education. Public school classes have been created for those whose handicap is of a temporary nature such as the slow convalescent from rheumatic fever and for those with such permanent impairments as cerebral palsy. Programs used in private schools, where for years education had been complemented by medical and therapeutic practices, have now been refined and included in public day schools. Special equipment of all kinds has been included in the school budget. Individualized transportation to permit spinal bifida or muscular dystrophy children to be enrolled in small classes has been arranged.

"I was aware that these children needed educational help," said one state governor, "but because of the added expense involved, I dreaded passage of the legislation. Personally, I knew it was necessary. Politically, I found myself delaying its promotion. Now, I'm one of its greatest exponents. Our classes for the physically handicapped often include those who are mentally retarded. At first, a few of these classes opened with only five children. I remember a particular one—a cerebral-palsied girl, two victims of polio in wheelchairs, one with muscular dystrophy, and a boy, whose hydrocephalic head had to be supported by a stiff collar, all learning together. Except for occasional visits, not one had ever been out of the home before—nor had any one of them ever had the joy of playing with another child. Today, that lad with hydrocephalus is earning several dollars a week putting bows on babies' booties. 'Impossible,' I would have said at one time. Now I know what is thought to be impossible can become a reality—but it takes all of us to make it possible."

Expensive? Yes. But, can anyone equate dollars and cents with the life and love of a child? Today educational programs for the mentally retarded have become one of the hallmarks of comprehensive, effective education—adjustment, maximum functioning, and independence for every child. Teachers of the retarded understand that his mind must be developed, his body strengthened and his character nourished in order that he, as an American citizen, may reach his ultimate potentiality. This new conception has resulted in many changes, one of which was introduced by Dr. Henry Goddard of the Training School at Vineland, New Jersey. By developing psychological research in the classroom and approving emphasis on individuality and nonacademic instruction, he opened new doors of opportunity for the retarded. "Happiness first and all else follows" became the motto of this famous school, for he proved that true education can only take place in an atmosphere of enthusiasm, happiness, and concrete motivation. Today we know that the same environment is essential for all learning.

It is impossible to mention the names of all those whose

outstanding work for the retarded has resulted in benefits for the normal, but one outstanding example is that of Dr. Meta Anderson Post, a graduate of teacher training at Vineland. As director of the Binet Classes in the public schools of Newark, New Jersey, she prepared for the retarded an ungraded sequence of kindergarten, departmental, and vocational work, centered upon self-care, activities in everyday life, speech training, manual dexterity, and practical academic work. By relating her students to the community, she trained them vocationally for local industries. The principles she evolved, following her own logic of continual improvisation, greatly influenced the teaching techniques for normal children as well as retarded.

In 1922, W. E. Fernald persuaded the state of Massachusetts to set up a statewide system of mental clinics for discovering and diagnosing mentally retarded children, which included advice as to educational objectives. These clinics provided the patterns for and the beginning of what later became known as child guidance clinics. This advanced technique proved that if additional opportunities for child growth and development are to take place, the teacher must be capable of creating an environment which enables each child to feel that school is a place where he belongs, where he is accepted, and where he is secure.

For years people felt that the elementary period was too early for children to start developing their self-concepts and to begin searching for themselves. Special services for pupils have shown that the process is well under way even before the child enters school. This is particularly true for the gifted child. We need to help children accept them-

selves, always keeping in mind that children may even de-
spise an outstanding talent if their giftedness makes them
different from others. Our duty is to help them achieve
self-concepts creatively rather than by authority, so as not
to mind being different from others.

Teachers across the nation now realize that no two
classes, regular or special, can be exactly alike. No two
children can be treated the same. No two problem situations can be identical. Some pupils receive speech, physical,
or occupational therapy along with their classroom assign-
ments. Other children, who may not require therapy, need
special assistance of a less obvious nature so that they may
overcome an emotional handicap. Still others need only
the care and protection of a sheltered environment and
the attention of an understanding and patient teacher. A
normal child crawls about his home, walks around his
neighborhood independently, accompanies his parents to
the store and to town, is able to manipulate objects and
play with other children of his own age. This is not true,
however, for all retarded. By and large they are less mature than the normal because they have lacked many normal experiences. Thus emphasis in the type of instruction
has had to be adjusted to suit their readiness for learning
and a much more gradual technique of introducing new
subjects brought into the lesson plans.

Our retarded, therefore, are teaching us that we dare
not generalize about persons except for purposes of research or statistics. We need this lesson, for since World
War II particularly, and on an ever-increasing scale since
the onset of automation, we have fallen into the habit of
grouping human beings without considering their moti-

vations, capacities and abilities. Regardless of the basic reason for a soldier having been considered unfit for service, when his military classification was "4F" we, too, began thinking of him as "4F" mentally, socially, and economically. Then we began dehumanizing individual personal characteristics and needs by talking about "parents of retarded children," "delinquent adolescents," "the unemployed," and "the deprived," as groups, forgetting that each person is different from every other. Today we speak, too, of "the aged," identifying them thus as soon as they become eligible for Social Security as if they were all decrepit and useless.

"I have a certain resistance to being segregated and it grows as I grow older," said one social welfare worker. "For this reason, I now understand why my clients go into a shell when I speak of them as 'my aged group.' There are some, of course, who because of special difficulties do not recognize that they might be considered elderly. There are those who need only home protection. They, too, would be shocked if you told them that they need care. Then, of course, there are those who are already receiving institutional care, but who could be returned to their homes. Many times, in lack of understanding, I confuse the issue because I prejudge people by chronological age, neglecting to recognize their individual problems."

His comments remind us in some ways of those so vehemently spoken by a young lady on her return from Europe. "They gave me one look while I was overseas and called me 'an American tourist, a flourishing, wealthy, single woman who wastes money in luxurious travel.' I hated the implication of being an Ugly American. True,

I saved my money and toured Denmark, but I made the trip because I wanted to learn how they care for their retarded. I want to be known for what I really am—the first teacher of an elementary Special Class for Trainable Children, the first of its kind in our school. If I could be objective and analyze my new sensitivity, no doubt it would stem from my experience with these children. Each is a personality all its own and they've taught me to treat others as I know they want to be treated."

At last we are learning that a long period of successive but painful episodes, each more frightening in its impact if not understood at the time, can hinder and even prevent development of an individual. Beginning before kindergarten, a child may cease to respond or take initiative when with other playmates or show any indication of sharing responsibility. In the first grade he is frightened and restless. As a member of a "no-book" family, his score on the intelligence test may be quite low. The cards are then stacked against him. Without a diploma, at the age of sixteen or less, he may drop out of school two grades behind those of his own age. His teachers, guidance counselors, principal, and others are frustrated and disappointed but far less than their pupil. Now considered incompetent and useless, he has little reason for living. He has failed educationally, but is it his fault?

Members of the President's Panel have emphasized that most of our so-called "retarded" come from low-income homes. We acknowledge the facts they present, and we, as members of society, realize that this socio-economic problem is grave, for it represents a waste of human talent.

Children are just as sensitive as adults in their reaction

to the pressures of poverty. They know when they are being considered socially and financially inferior. It brings deep hurt, and the result can be far more devastating than many physical disabilities. Society accepts those who are broken in limb but not always those whose wounds are not obvious to the naked eye. The ravages of discontent are often too profound to make any simple type of psychological or therapeutic help of value. In other words, this child fights for survival. Finally, due to his inability to cope with life, because he fails we classify him as "retarded." In reality it is because he has never been given sufficient and continued help to achieve.

In our society the trend is from dependence toward independence. If one is frustrated in his desire to become independent he shows distress, which in a child must be considered a normal reaction. Neither school nor home has been what it should be. Something better must be devised. Classes for such children may have to be scheduled on a biweekly basis for two or three hours. The schedule must be flexible enough to allow the child to go home, if necessary, before association with others becomes too frightening for him. Hopefully with time the hours can lengthen and schedules become more regular. Special activities available for other children may have to be reduced or eliminated so that the child has a chance to regain confidence in one teacher. This type of program would also provide an opportunity for better control of his environment.

Adults play differing roles in society, but it is adults who continue to say "children must be students from this to that age, and must conform to prearranged schedules."

What a child can accomplish in school should be the achievement which will outbalance failures met elsewhere in life. At first we needed legislation to provide Special Education. This we have. More recently educators have been laying stress on better class standards, but administrators are still too prone to solve problems of local and parent pressure by any device that can bring immediate temporary relief. Any loose eligibility policy, any instructor with little or no preparation, any room with little or no attention to safety requirements and any promotion of a curriculum which includes generalizing teaching methods not adaptable to the individual needs of each child is wrong. Moreover, a teaching method which aids one retarded child does not necessarily help another.

Today the number of pupils in our public school classes makes the tutorial method impossible. Good teachers, however, do strive to satisfy at least to some extent the educational needs of each individual child. They attempt to discover why he may not respond well. They encourage and explain subjects as clearly as possible. Unfortunately their goal is not always achieved in large classes or even in some of the smaller specialized classes. The teaching machine may be a help.

The first mechanical device to provide individualized training for normal children appeared almost a half century ago. In 1920, Sidney L. Pressey invented a machine for the purpose of presenting to students a series of statements and questions, one at a time. The pupil was permitted four possible answers—the correct one could be identified by pushing one of four buttons. If he selected the wrong one, the next statement and question would not appear. This machine might have become widely used by schools except that few people then recognized the importance of the individual needs of each child. During the following thirty years two things occurred: first, many educators began to seek solution to the serious problem of overcrowding in all our schools; and second, psychologists began conducting research relating to the learning of both retarded and normal children.

Dr. B. F. Skinner, of Harvard University, in 1950 devised a machine which rewarded pigeons when they responded in a desired fashion. Later, when he became interested in his own daughter's mathematical achievements, he wondered whether by using an individualized and instantaneous reward her progress could be speeded up. He therefore developed a teaching machine, similar to the one invented in 1920, which rewarded the pupil by means of a signal for each correct response given. As soon as his daughter began using it, he noted that she derived so much interest from following a pattern of her own that she proceeded from one question to another, not waiting for additional instruction. The experiment proved that his daughter when working alone could learn arithmetic more quickly and more thoroughly than when in a classroom with other pupils.

Although the question-and-answer technique was not new, watching his daughter develop her skill confirmed his belief that it was no longer necessary to force all children into a rigid lockstep pattern of training. Several things became apparent to Dr. Skinner. If, because of being retarded, a child could only learn slowly, this machine could be the means of teaching him slowly but well; if the child were emotionally disturbed, it could engage his attention and help prevent his overactivity; in the case of the gifted child, it could increase his rate of learning. An individual student, regardless of his ability, would neither be pulled ahead too quickly nor held back. "Programming" the course of instruction from simple to more complex questions would make it possible for able students to proceed in accordance with their own abilities, permitting them to complete a course in three weeks, four months, or if necessary, the customary allotted time period of a full school year. In a democracy such as ours, this "teaching machine" offers a revolutionary means to provide precise regard for the individual physical and mental needs of every pupil.

Although first developed to assist a normal child learn more quickly and easily, the use of the machine with retarded children has taught us many new lessons.

"I am sure there is nothing mentally wrong with Bill," said a mother who was concerned about her son, "but he is thirteen years old and he still cannot read!" After the counselor had talked with the child, she decided that his ability to read had been thwarted for five years, not because of mental retardation but because of the manner in which he had been receiving instruction.

"I am going to teach you in a different way," she said. "Would you be willing to help me?"

He agreed to use the teaching machine. In three weeks he was learning to recognize words. In six weeks, he was reading well enough to rejoin his classmates in the seventh grade. The change in his rate of learning may be considered miraculous. In reality, it was due directly to the fact that his basic emotional need for encouragement to achieve had been recognized and taken into consideration.

One mentally retarded child, who had been unable to speak prior to use of this individualized rewarding system, began talking within three weeks. He began to recognize word symbols, and in less than a month was able to read sentences. At home, because he had been chastised for his inability to communicate, he was unwilling even to try to speak. When asked by his father about the change, he replied, "The machine doesn't yell at me. You did. I'm not deaf."

In the majority of our classrooms the slow student is forced to digest the same amount of information in the same amount of time as the more able student. If because of a reading difficulty he cannot keep up with the class, he tends to skip difficult material. When given the opportunity to use a teaching machine, he is permitted to read at a slower rate. The amount of practice required for each item may be adjusted to the extent a student has mastered that portion of the lesson. Each time his answer is correct the knowledge becomes imbedded in his mind. He is thus enabled to continue until he knows he has attained a perfect score before proceeding to a new assignment.

This is a much stronger learning process than that in which a pupil hurriedly studies to complete a lesson, takes an examination at the end of the week or month, then waits several days to learn his grade. The sooner his answers are confirmed, the more effectively his learning is reinforced. Opponents of this new learning process may say that the normal curve for grading examinations will be directly affected if each student achieves one hundred in a test. But which is more important, our traditional grading system or the development of individual ability?

The emphasis placed on the speed with which a person can complete a task, although it does provide an indication of his ability, should not mean as much to us as just *how* he performs when under stress.

"If only she had given me a few more minutes," complained one elementary child to his mother. "I know I could have finished those questions. Now, no matter what I tell her she won't ever let me get into the fifth grade." Not only does this pressure cause lower grades for many normal slow-learning pupils but, if continued, it can also cause fear of all future testing procedures. Emotional tensions are bound to decrease when we give children time for thought and time in which to complete their tasks. A teaching machine allows them to take utmost advantage of their own abilities—permitting them to proceed at their own rate of speed and enabling the teacher to give every child more personalized attention.

It is still as difficult to provide special services for gifted pupils as for the mentally retarded. In many places an attempt to solve the problem has been made by dividing students into two or more separate groups, the more gifted in one and the less able in another. This procedure has certain drawbacks. Even the most gifted student does not always do well in every subject. Perhaps in a science course he may fall farther and farther behind in his studies, although in English and history he achieves the highest grades. In the one class he needs specific and individualized help to achieve as well as in the other subjects. A programing device would permit half of the students in a class to work with their machines while the teacher is instructing others. At the Point Park Junior College in Pittsburgh, it was found that the failing rate in a medical technology class had dropped from 12 percent to 3 percent after teaching machines were introduced. The percentage of A and B students rose from 50 to 85, and the students were found to be completing courses in 30 rather than the usual 120 hours.

Democratic goals of education are frequently criticized for having lowered or leveled our standards and achievements. Other critics state that the problems created by an ever-increasing student load have led some schools to abandon these goals and to concentrate on training of the intellectually elite. Both the gifted and the retarded are thus compromised by our traditional school system, traditional classroom, and traditional textbooks. Large-scale use of tested programs using teaching machines may make it possible to cope with our growing educational program and at the same time raise our educational standards for the gifted pupil, thereby achieving a higher intellectual level in our society.

It is still necessary for teachers to devote a considerable portion of their week's work to the grading of examinations and to detailed preparation of reports. Much of this drudgery could be automatically eliminated by use of a teaching machine, which can tabulate items in one rapid operation. It also permits more frequent short tests as contrasted to longer examinations given at the end of the week or term.

In our planning for the future we must, however, keep one very important fact in mind. Despite its usefulness, the teaching machine, as with audio-visual aids and our ever-increasing use of classroom TV, cannot replace the teacher. Nothing can compare or ever will be as important in the life of a child as the way a teacher influences his learning or future destiny! Progressive steps in modern teaching methods need never be considered a threat to the teaching profession—they merely provide a better means of training.

Children who have extreme difficulty in communicating with others, in addition to learning how to speak, require considerable help in learning how to live more comfortably and agreeably in their own homes. They require assistance in developing desirable personal attitudes toward friends and others. One little girl of six stuttered so badly that she refused to participate in the classroom activities. After using the machine for only three days, of her own volition she returned to class and, to the amazement of the teacher, began answering questions without stuttering. Her progress continued for several weeks, save for one strange factor. Early each morning, when she returned to school, she would begin the day by stuttering. Then, for some unexplained reason her stuttering would stop. The teacher investigated the family relationship and learned that the child's speech had been directly affected by an overbearing, far more intelligent older sister.

"Joan," asked the teacher, "were you afraid at first that we would make fun of you?"

"Yes," replied the child. "At home, the more I tried, the more they laughed. You didn't laugh and the machine didn't laugh."

If, when using the teaching machine, only the grade

that a child makes on an assignment is noted, without also taking into consideration the emotional growth of the child, a very important part of its value is lost. Statistical measurement of the achievement made is not enough. The teacher must also obtain detailed knowledge about the ability and opportunity which the child has had and will have to apply the material studied to other elements of his experience. He must also be able to account for failure.

Whether used with retarded or gifted, the two extremes which administrators generally believe can benefit most, teaching machines will never serve as a crutch for our children. Every child needs to be helped to observe and evaluate details. A mechanical device cannot pump information into a person's mind. Every learning program is made up by a person highly trained to present the proper stimuli for the purpose of obtaining desired and correct responses. As a typewriter is only a bridge which provides the mind with a swift way to introduce thoughts to the page, so a teaching machine is a bridge which permits an instructor to serve as a private tutor to many students at the same time.

We live in a world of people, not a laboratory of machines. Despite the less than 10 percent of our educators who still think that this technique has no permanent value, we now know that it can provide the necessary confidence required to return some pupils to a class group with a good chance of success. It can, if used wisely and well, free teachers for their unique roles of preparing the youth of our nation to become better citizens.

Our retarded have made us accept the problems of individual differences and the necessity of providing a suitable curriculum for normal or retarded children based on these differences in intellectual ability. They have also proven that any curriculum designed for the educable mentally retarded or normal child should be periodically modified as employment needs are modified. Tomorrow's children hopefully will have had more education than they have had in the past, a greater exposure to prevocational training when necessary, and their families will have been given a better understanding of adolescent and young adult needs. However, much of this will depend upon the way in which individual schools and individual teachers develop their programs, take advantage of new available resources, use imagination and creativeness. This is far more important than the continued use of any accepted theory or generalization. All services must be planned with one goal in mind: "Will this training produce fulfillment of their basic need for personal dignity?"

If, beginning with preschool vocabulary training on through the elementary and high school grades, the use of teaching machines could become an integral part of our educational program, certain pupils could complete the customary twelve-year course in less time. In relation to our present-day emphasis on science, this would have a dramatic effect on our society, for it could provide additional funds for both college and graduate levels of training.

From the standpoint of other nations, its effective use by teachers we send overseas could be equally revolutionary. Though but a drop in the bucket of illiteracy, we spend roughly one hundred million dollars a year to provide educational assistance to other countries. Due to the immense problems faced by teachers who represent us, little time can be devoted to adjusting to the individual needs of each student. A great percentage of our Peace Corps workers are agriculture and language teachers. How much more could be accomplished if they could be provided with this additional educational tool?

Most manufacturing companies prepare and distribute information for customers about the correct use of their product or equipment. When the purchaser of a new car is given a booklet of instruction, often he will glance through it searching only for those sections which are new to him. It is unnecessary for him to read the entire booklet because as a rule he is familiar with its contents.

In the same fashion, the Bell Telephone Company always includes in its directories several pages, usually accompanied by small photographs, describing the use of the dial instrument. Though formerly the majority of customers seldom found it necessary to refer to these instructions, now many people check them before initiating the recently established direct long distance dialing system. For normal children and adults, particularly those who can read English, the present type of written instructions are simple to follow. However, there are many people who find it necessary to obtain supplemental instruction.

Use of a "teaching aid" for these customers has been considered by several companies. For example, recently the Bell Telephone and Singer Sewing Machine companies have made tentative arrangements with the Devereux Foundation, Institute for Research and Training, at Devon, Pennsylvania, for permission to use lesson materials now under experimentation with mentally retarded and emotionally disturbed children.

Parents of school children are frequently the same persons who initiate legislative and organizational improvements for school programs and employ the school staff. In the light of recent experience it is time that they re-evaluate mandates for pupil enrollment and provide for extension of any and all methods which will improve instruction. The question to be answered is: Does our present state legislation, local administrative policy and budgetary provision prevent educators from helping *every* child to mature? If the answer is positive then we are not preparing them for life—the ultimate goal of education.

CHAPTER VI

DESIGN FOR LIVING

Though their many-sided facets are well known to millions of war casualties, to thousands each year whose bodies are shattered as a result of accident, and to the continually mounting score of stroke victims, personal rehabilitative needs remain a mystery to many people. Why? Because our concept remains clouded by our own interests and responsibilities. We concentrate more on how the person affects us than on the total effect we produce on him before, during and after his restorative period. To one he remains "my child," to another, "my patient," to someone else, "my client," and to still another, "the job applicant whom I must treat differently if I hire him."

Realistically, what is rehabilitation? It is the difference between living and existing. As one recently blinded woman said: "To me it was the re-creation of hope, health and happiness. Not just regaining my sight, for that I will never have again. Rehabilitation is renewal of self-determination, self-reliance, and the return of freedom from control of others."

Emotionally, socially, and economically, her personal definition is sound, but to those who love and work with retarded persons rehabilitation implies far more—the expectation of new performance. In addition to restorative services for those who have physical disabilities, the cerebral palsied retarded, those with epileptic seizures, the retarded deaf, the retarded with speech impairments, and others with secondary disabling conditions, it includes an enabling, habilitative process. This concept lays stress on the possibility of new functioning rather than focusing attention on the retardate's inability or incapacity, for how can one restore a function which has never been present? Instead of our old negative attitude which in a sense superimposed social retardation upon a person's mental retardation, this positive approach can prevent him from becoming so "disabled" as to be considered a community handicap. Many of our estimated five and a half million retarded children and adults have need of rehabilitative and habilitative services. Not all require both. Those over twenty-one years of age have never been able to attend special classes, nor have they had the privilege of receiving vocational training programs—these persons need habilitative services. For them a new and not a restorative program is required.

Does this mean a different life only in terms of what a person can do for himself? No. Rehabilitation has never been achieved alone. It requires the help of others. Rehabilitation is a process which inspires and induces an individual to realize his full potential, be he retarded, mentally ill, physically handicapped, a nonconformist to the rules of society, or a so-called normal individual. It is society's service to each of its members—a society which dares to dream and drive toward the goal of a full life for every person. It involves the deep-rooted feelings of a family and the community, a concern about and assistance with the solving of individual problems which when provided can stimulate and if denied can deter the development of any person's progress. The crucial factor in rehabilitation is not the question of whether a person will succeed in fulfilling all his needs, but the position taken by society about this unique individual.

Helen Keller has suggested that the attitude of the seeing toward the blind is more difficult to bear than the handicap of blindness. Individually, our basic concern in the process must be to determine whether the plans and decisions which affect the child or adult are for his good, and not necessarily how they may change our own lives. As applied to our fellowmen it may mean that at times we must contribute to the development of a rehabilitation service which can improve the lot of other handicapped persons and not our own loved one. Demand for a specific type of community service, that which is best for the majority, may not be what we personally desire most but one to which we must give time. Parents who have watched their retarded child grow have been forced to learn this difficult lesson of service. When their child was the age of three they wanted preschool services, as he reached school age they voted for special class instruction, and it was not until he became an adolescent and his need for vocational training became apparent that they became willing to support a community sheltered workshop program. They were drifting in time—not looking into the future for themselves or for others.

"John's changing needs," wrote one mother, "taught me that if I acted solely on my immediate interests, other retardates in our community would be prevented from making progress. Now I am working toward the opening of a rehabilitation center for the physically handicapped. Services we expect to provide won't benefit John but because my vision has been broadened, were it a center for retarded I couldn't work harder. One of the staff jokingly said he thought I'd been emotionally rehabilitated. He was so right. Surgical wounds can heal with time, but emotional wounds open again and again as a retarded child faces new difficulties. Though eventually I reached a plateau of acceptance, until recently I gave very little thought to the problems of others. I'm now trying to help other parents become 'rehabilitated.' We parents have needs, too."

The creation of a will to help others born from a womb of sorrow can be multiplied a millionfold. No better example can be found than that of Henry Viscardi, Jr., founder and president of a living monument to courage, Abilities, Inc., which employs over four hundred severely handicapped people, including retarded, and grosses over two million dollars a year. His was a dream—the dream of being able to walk tall. Born without legs yet daring to do well, he completed elementary and high school in eight years, attended Fordham University, and after two years took a job as a law clerk. After many unsuccessful attempts to be fitted with artificial appliances and still only two feet eight inches tall, at the age of twenty-six he was given height.

Eleven years ago in a vacant garage in the village of West Hempstead, Long Island, he began a noble, unprecedented venture, the founding of Abilities, Inc. "We asked no charity," said Mr. Viscardi as he reminisced one day, "no support of any kind; instead, we borrowed eight thousand dollars for the enterprise. We decided we would pay prevailing wages, would compete for our contracts, that we wouldn't weave rugs or make baskets, but that we would build complex components in the electronics industry, using only the most severely disabled people we could find, those who would be unemployable by any other business. . . . We began with four employees. Among the four we had but one usable leg and four usable arms. The usable leg was on one employee whose other leg was disarticulated at the hip and one of whose arms was off at the shoulder." *

Amazing things have happened since that late summer of 1952. When Abilities celebrated its tenth anniversary, 456 employees covered by all the emoluments of enlightened industry were occupying their own air-conditioned building. The products they had manufactured were valued at $16,000,000. If these same employees had been on relief it is estimated the cost would have been over $4,000,000 for the same period.

"This is nothing," says the man whose fabric and creation of a dream brought dignity and happiness to men and

* Henry Viscardi, "Address," *Proceedings of the Third Pennsylvania Conference of the Governor's Committee for the Handicapped,* November 27, 1962, p. 29.

women who might always have been dependent upon others. "I say again, nothing compared to the example and lesson we have given to American industry. What we have done is to base our program on the philosophy of love. For my money, the key to successful motivation is the simple four-letter word—love. Love for man's dignity. Love for his right to be the same and not different from the rest of the world. Love for his right to support himself, and not be supported. . . . Abilities, Incorporated, has stood for an almost forgotten word in American industry— integrity. There is a sense of purpose and dedication among these people which exceeds anything I have seen anywhere in American industry, and as a result, a product is produced with integrity, integrity in the product, integrity and belief in the company, integrity in the belief of the destiny of each individual who works for it." *

Now even more dramatically Hank Viscardi and his associates are demonstrating to the world what can be done by those who dare to try. Copies of Abilities exist in New Zealand, Australia, South America, South Africa, Japan, and two in France.

To develop research and teaching arms in Abilities, a sister corporation was formed seven years ago, the Human Resources Foundation. Housed in an entirely separate building and directed by a paraplegic from polio, the purpose of this enterprise included development of better methods and goals for utilizing the potentials of retardates both for white- and blue-collar jobs. One project, supported in part by the research and demonstration grant funds from the Office of Vocational Rehabilitation, in-

* *Ibid.*, p. 30.

volved training and working with basic tools and equipment used in a typical electronics plant such as Abilities, Inc. This particular study involved fifteen retarded youngsters who at the time were attending a special class for educable children in addition to the young adult retarded group employed in the plant.

The program for these children conducted four hours a day for a full school year began with an explanation of the job skills to be learned and of the needs of retarded persons to the foreman for whom the person would be working in competition with other employees. Training and working at simulated work areas including many difficult processes, even those requiring recognition and proper use of parts necessary for the assembling of a transistor radio.

Though audio-visual training devices were used on an exploratory basis, it was found that by continued repetition verbal and visual instructions were more readily understood and less confusion evidenced because the instructions could be kept consistent. By programming the entire training on colored slides and tape, even adults functioning at about the third-grade level gained instruction with enthusiasm and accuracy.

These are the sorts of things which can be the reward of giving the liberty of reason to a childhood dream. For dreams are not all, as Churchill once said, "only children of the night, of indigestion bred." Nor are dreams always playful dust of the brain, ignored impressions of the day's events which during sleep become keenly illuminated with a new and frightening significance. Dreams can be a magnificent property of the mind which through personal honesty can reveal a stark awareness of need, and then, with courage and daring can produce action!

In the ancient books of the Vedas it is said that action follows thought even as the cartwheel follows the bullock's hoof. Life did something to Hank Viscardi but he did something to life. In that moment of truth when as a lad he realized he was not the same as others, he mobilized his own personality, he decided what he wanted, what he wanted to be and what he was going to do. There must have been clouding of the inward man, days in which he walked as if in a dark wood but he held to his dreams and dared!

Emotional and physical curative services to the orthopedically handicapped have provided us with a clearer picture of what should be done for our retarded. Lessons learned at the Institute for the Crippled and Disabled and the Altro Workshops in New York City about tubercular, postcardiac, and, more recently, discharged mental patients have altered our preconceived opinions of long-range vocational plans. One retardate may have a personal need for an activity center program but still require some travel training and related self-care functions. Others, in addition to training relating to social activities, may require personalized service of a totally different type. Some may benefit most from sheltered employment, group job-training, or in a vast number of cases, actual placement in normal jobs within the community.

Nationwide statistics indicate that most retarded persons rehabilitated into employment work in service occupations, unskilled jobs, and semi-skilled work. About a fourth of all retardates ready for competitive employment secure opportunities in clerical, sales, skilled jobs, agricultural work, and service as family workers or homemakers. Though it cannot be predicted whether these occupations will alter in the future, as we gradually learn how better to prepare them for suitable employment one thing is clear, the number of trained and employable retardates will steadily increase. The full effects of automation have yet to be felt, and in general its effects on the retarded are yet to be evaluated. We can be sure, however, that despite automation there will always be a need for workers in the service areas, in which the mentally retarded have consistently had their greatest success.

One interesting research project conducted within the past few years in Altoona, Pennsylvania, involved a study of post-school adjustment and employment of 1,500 former Special Education pupils. As a result of interviews with both the employee and employer it was found that 30 percent of the retardates declined to admit former membership in Special Education classes because they might then be considered unacceptable. Fifty-nine percent had secured their present jobs through the efforts of relatives or friends, 15 percent through their own efforts, and only 2 percent with the help of the school. The average salary was $3,327. From the wage distribution it was determined that 42 percent of those employed had equaled or exceeded the starting salary for a beginning teacher with four years of college training. Sixty-four percent of the eligible males had been inducted into the military service, where they had been promoted, attended and taught classes, and in general developed into mature, independent young men. Fifty-one percent had savings accounts, 24 percent maintained checking accounts, and 73 percent were listed on charge accounts; 84 percent had life insurance; 73 percent were on the rolls of Blue Cross; and, far more to their credit, 25 percent either owned or were in the process of buying homes.

When compared at that time with other employees who ranged from a laundry presser at $832 per year to a tractor-trailer driver receiving an annual salary of $7,800, 2 to 9 percent were rated below average; 52 to 77 percent as average; and 15 to 45 percent above average. These comparisons were based on grooming, courtesy, desirable reaction to criticism, effort, memory for directions, punctuality, responsibility, and speed.

This study is particularly interesting because many retarded are fired from jobs mainly for deficiencies in work habits, rather than failure to be able to do the work. Among the many goals for gainful employment of retardates is that of being able to get to and from work on time and to have enough flexibility so that they can tolerate any necessary changes in routine.

There are a comparative few of the retarded who will never be able to achieve independence. Some will always be unable to participate in normal community activities. But to the degree to which each person can participate he must be given a chance. If he is unable to care for his own needs and unable to assume any responsibility, certainly vocational planning would be unsuitable. For such a person the goal should be "independent living." For those who with assistance can accomplish simple tasks, regardless of the time it may require for training, this accomplishment should be considered the ultimate goal. Nothing should deter us from providing necessary training regardless of the achievement each may or may not attain.

Unfortunately the staffing and standards of sheltered workshop programs have varied as widely as the terminology used to describe the program. Some provide only terminal employment for disabled persons; others have added vocational evaluation and specific job training; still others provide a comprehensive rehabilitation service, including social casework, medical and psychological examinations, vocational counseling and living quarters. A large number serve only specific disability groups, such as the blind, the cerebral palsied, or the retarded. A new philosophy is emerging. Some subcontracts, which cannot be fulfilled by a single disability workshop, it has been learned, can be completed by the combination of a variety of severely disabled persons, no one of whom contributes much individually, but together form an efficient productive unit.

There have been instances where disabled workers have been exploited to undercut the market for goods and services in which the workshop functions, even times when one workshop has undercut another in the same community. Rehabilitation is not a profit-making venture—it is a humane community responsibility. As such, where a workshop is in existence, or the creation of one is being contemplated, the community must assume responsibility, share in the planning, share in the operating policies, and share in any expenses not covered by fees. Only then can we expect to make this occupational endeavor sound. A U. S. Children's Bureau report of 1960 indicates that within a decade, of the more than 6,500,000 retarded in our country at least one-half will be children. During the lifetime of this group, at one time or another 10 percent, or 650,000, will require services offered by a sheltered workshop.

From these facts, plus experiences gleaned from retarded persons employed in workshops, not only must we face the need for a greatly expanded program for those who will require long-range employment but we must also improve the key relationship which now exists between parents and workshop personnel. At first, and in the main, parents contributed to the creation, development, management, and sometimes even the staffing of these occupational centers. As workshops grew and became staffed with professionals, a power struggle began. Policies regarding finances were questioned. Delicate differences of opinion arose about those persons who should be continued as so-called employees. It is now time that we as parents or relatives of retarded persons recognize the fact that we are no longer needed to staff these programs. Instead we must accept new roles and satisfactions if the total overall program is to progress to a useful level.

In general, informed parents will cooperate. For example, the reward earned by a retarded or handicapped person is of tremendous importance to him, regardless of the amount of the paycheck. When good family-centered programs are established, parents will cooperate by purposefully helping to handle the monies their child has received, recognizing them as an integral part of the total rehabilitative process. And, as each family is stimulated to help in the development of more productive sheltered workshop programs, community receptiveness of the need for such employment opportunities will increase. This in turn can help agency personnel in the adjustment of their professional and administrative routines so that without misunderstandings vocational needs of persons and their families may be met.

Strangely enough, there is another phase of rehabilitation which we have tended to neglect—the part which recreation can play in establishing and stimulating a person's energy, initiative, and the use of his total self. All play and art reflect the values of the civilization which gave them birth. They go further, for the values we absorb in our games are carried into other areas of our lives and form the bases of other relationships. Recreation can teach a person to laugh and be joyful in the use of his muscles. It can help him to be himself, to achieve self-expression and develop a personality. Each person moves at his own pace. Activities which interest one child may not interest another, but the manner in which retarded children have developed when given the opportunity to play has taught us that barriers between adults can be broken in the same way.

Now, with employment trends altering, society must approach recreation not only as part of a child's life or as one way in which homebound people can spend their leisure but also as a problem which we must consider for all those who in the future will not be working. It may very well be that with increased automation a great portion of our normal population will be at leisure half the time, while the other half is employed. It is time to begin thinking not only about what a man will do when he reaches the age of retirement but about what the coming generations will do with their leisure.

There was a time when we thought of rehabilitation only as it applied to someone who was physically handicapped. Then we dared to think of this concept in relation to the mentally retarded and the mentally ill. In reality each of us at some time in our lives needs some form of rehabilitative service. It could be when our bodies are encumbered by pain. At such a time it can be strangely dulling and subduing to awaken to another day that must be spent between walls and under one roof. Pains too small to presume to knock at the door of heaven, but not too small for one to wish they might be extensive enough to be discussed with another, can sadly cramp the soul. It is then that all pleasant dreams are laid waste.

In a similar fashion, the reversal of an important decision can devastate, particularly if the power of decision rests entirely in the hands of others. The trouble could be the loss of means—for poverty can be a stifling darkness. Then there is the tragedy of bereavement. As Queen Victoria in the days of her early widowhood piteously described it to Dean Stanley: "Always wishing to consult one who is not here, groping by myself, with a constant sense of desolation." It appeared to her during those days that her dreams had vanished and life had become but one long night of loneliness. Those who have gone through this valley know that, as with the restoration of the body, to become normal again while the weeks slowly and relentlessly pass, one reaches different emotional and physical levels of acceptance.

No one, either by forcing or preaching, can make a bereaved person hold to his dream during that period, for it is then, as with any handicapped individual, the soul receives only that which it asks for and is ready to receive. It is the same with parents of a retarded child. They, too, must reach a different plane before they can accept the disappointment of not having given birth to a normal child. So it is with a healthy person, man or woman, who has never been ill or contemplated sickness—and then is cut down in the prime of life.

When nerves of the body are severed, at first there is no feeling, but when pain follows it is searing in quality. Though needed medical attention is given, and finally the nerve-cord to a dream of a rich, full life returns to normal, one begins to sharpen the knife of pain by remembering jubilant yesterdays. Courage is not easy. At such a time all the person can do is become more deeply immersed in a cavern of hopelessness. Despite encouragement about the probable return to health, particularly if he has lost a portion of his body, he listens with deaf ears to those who say he will again live a normal life. Even walking examples of determination do not interest him.

One thing of which we are sure—restorative or habilitative gains are seldom achieved singly. They require the help of others, yet such assistance must be *practical, timely, and acceptable* to the disabled person. This past summer two orthopedic patients were overheard discussing their mutual problems. "They might as well do a good job in the operating room while they are at it," remarked one man to his friend. "Fact is, without either leg all I'm good for is horsemeat." The despondent comment, though harsh, was treated by the nursing staff as merely an emotional explosion far preferable to silence. Instead of sympathizing or reprimanding him they recognized that the bitter remarks were normal. Today he is proudly walking through the corridors of the hospital.

This is no different from the patient who upon learning the number of weeks she was to remain bedfast in the hospital immediately prepared a calendar. Day after day she reviewed the allotted time, prolonging each week as a prisoner would his sentence. Sympathy would have been spurned and recreational or occupational therapy greeted with disgust had either been offered. These are the sorts of things we must attempt to understand, for rehabilitation for others or for ourselves is a process. It does not happen overnight, be it a physical, emotional or mental restoration, but the dreams must continue.

Where would society be today without men and women who have dared to dream? In Maryland, because a few so-called dreamers were willing to alter the beautician law, which prevented retarded educable girls from working in beauty shops, a licensure law was amended. Today opportunity is available for those same girls to receive training and work as employees. Personally and collectively we must keep our dreams growing. They are a design for living.

CHAPTER VII

CARE AWAY FROM HOME

Nothing in life can be as exacting in its tragic results or as rewarding in its benefits as the manner in which one human being treats another. A good human relationship, mutually helpful, is the greatest of all undertakings and requires the use of our best powers, Alas, although history is full of the results of man's compassion to man, it also records his inhumanity.

As a society, we are drifting away from the individual care at home to institutionalization of those who because of a long-term mental or physical infirmity or handicap are different. It has become a broad social trend. We began by placing and keeping the mentally ill and mentally retarded in large institutions regardless of their abilities. Then the chronically ill, and now elderly people find that they, too, are unwanted at home. Away from the sight and sound of love, persons who could be kept within the family circle when treated in this fashion slowly deteriorate mentally and physically.

The separation of both young and old, handicapped or non-handicapped persons, arouses anxiety. As with prisoners of war, shame and guilt replace reason. The panic produced in those thus segregated can result in severe withdrawal from the outside world in order to escape the despair of being alone. Later, death becomes the benefactor. Meanwhile, the personalities and characters of relatives and friends become hardened in the process. We cannot destroy other human beings without destroying ourselves, too.

Inhumanity is basically the result of the accumulated selfishness of many individuals. When we reject and relegate those whom we have loved, we add one more ripple to the ocean of cruelty, for many of these rejected persons with only a little help can live happy and perhaps useful lives in their own communities. Such selfishness is only highlighted by our increasing lack of sufficient institutional facilities, private schools, foster and boarding homes. Despite a tremendous expansion in building programs at present, the average state hospital for the mentally ill has 367 patients more than its rated capacity. In like manner, each institution for the retarded has a national average of 340 persons waiting for admittance. To cite but one example, in 1962 Kentucky's minimum need for residential services for the retarded was 4,600 beds, or 3,850 more than their facilities at that time were designed to accommodate. Authorities estimate this will increase. One wonders how far we would go in compounding our problems were it not for the comprehensive plans for mental health and mental retardation now being considered or in process by every state and territory.

What is the reason behind the rejection of the old and the handicapped? Sometime it is a lack of essential diagnostic instruments. Inadequate diagnosis may be postponed because of the scarcity of professional personnel with appropriate attitudes and training in a given field. In the case of the mentally retarded, for example, unless there are noticeable physical differences at birth, a competent analysis of the child's condition is essential in order to determine whether any abnormality exists. During the first six to eight months of a baby's life, particularly in cases of severe retardation or if it is a family where there are other children, parents usually discover that one child's development differs in certain ways from that of others. Slowness in sitting up or in walking, extreme fretfulness, or perhaps a series of unexplained seizures may arouse fear. In the absence of such signs, however, many parents are unaware of the situation until the child has been refused promotion from kindergarten or from the first grade. By then it may be too late, for as yet science knows of no way to replace injured, destroyed, or undeveloped brain cells. Therefore only from the results of thorough examinations made by a team of specialists can a parent be told accurately, through tests repeated from time to time, whether a child may be expected to live a life of *independence, be partially dependent or totally dependent.* Periods of care and study away from home may be necessary for certain complicated cases in order that organic and functional disturbances may be determined, diagnosis confirmed, and recommendations made for treatment. In any case, regardless of questions raised by the parents, *all* children should be given the advantage of comprehensive evaluation before placement in any institution and provided continued study while there.

No approach can prepare parents for the knowledge that their child is retarded, but the harsh truth must be told. Strong individuals become weak; others, supposedly weak, have exhibited unexpected strength and courage. It comes to all as a stunning blow. Like reflection upon impending death, when the fear becomes fact, it produces shock. How could it happen to us? The question asks itself and there is no answer. Yet the problem must be attacked.

There will, of course, always be a number of totally dependent persons who cannot be cared for at home. Their needs are best supplied in a more protective environment. Fortunately, a very small percentage of the retarded require such constant service and supervision. The decision as to whether the child should live at home or in an institution depends not only upon the condition of the person but also upon the individual family situation. Generally speaking, the most important factor is the degree of the child's needs and the level of retardation.

If the disability is very severe it can sometimes be determined at birth or in early infancy. The fact that mongolism can be diagnosed at birth, however, does not tell us the degree of retardation. Some mongoloid children are totally dependent but most of them are trainable and can live quite happily and usefully at home and in the community. Some parents are still unaware of this fact, since certain physicians still advise parents to place mongoloid babies in boarding homes or institutions. In such instances parents are not given a chance to learn how well these children can be trained to adapt to their own needs and become as is their right, an integral part of the family circle.

Upon receiving well-considered counsel and advice about their child's impaired or incomplete mental development, many parents feel a desperate need to go from one physician or psychologist to another, seeking a diagnosis they would prefer to hear. This is not the answer. It is not within the power of anyone to alter fact, and mature love requires the acceptance of truth.

To accept does not mean the dull sleepy acquiescence of indolence; instead, acceptance is the active willingness to help provide throughout life every possible service required to supply this child with the means for his fullest development. At Pineland Hospital and Training Center, Maine's only state facility, for example, such services are discussed with parents and relatives of retarded children. The requests they make are usually for information, not for placement. Despite the fact that most of the parents live in isolated, rural areas, obviously unable to supply their retarded children's needs, 79 percent prefer to keep them at home. Discussions about possible admittance to Pineland generally include only problems which might arise should the family situation alter. Forty percent pay for some sort of care for the children, and though many parents admit that it is often difficult to keep the child at home, they would be extremely resentful were they asked to place him in an institution.

As parents come to understand their retarded children, they tend increasingly to accept them and to keep them at home, at least as long as this is best for the child and family. More careful screening procedures are now given for admittance to state and private residential settings, and the obvious change in attitude by parents has meant that proportionately fewer retarded children are being crowded into institutions. Many who in previous years would have been separated from their families are now not even considered eligible for institutions.

There remain two major points of view on the separation of preschool severely retarded children from their families. One group insists that we should provide more public facilities to accommodate the retarded. They speak in terms of increased urbanization resulting in crowded living conditions, employment of mothers, improved institutional services, and the extended life-span of the severely retarded as a result of better medical care. More emphatically, they emphasize that a grossly handicapped person living at home can cause psychological damage to the other members of the family. Opponents of early residential care contend that the retarded child's need for love and affection, like that of normal children, is so basic that it must be fulfilled for the development of a healthy personality in spite of the handicap. This love they believe cannot be provided even in modernized facilities in view of understaffing and overcrowded conditions.

The solution to this problem is a compromise of the two ideas. Everyone agrees that neither public nor private residential care is an adequate substitute for love and careful training provided by an adequate family unit. But a firm stand that a retarded infant should never be separated from his family is no more satisfactory than if one were to assume that all identifiable retarded, emotionally disturbed, physically handicapped, and aged should be institutionalized. If keeping the child at home constitutes possible harm to the family, some provision should be made to place the child in a different setting. Society must demand this when necessary. Parental neglect, inadequate family resources, severe medical or behavioral problems are a few of the difficulties which prevent the possibility of choice. Where a choice can be made, a parent's code of values must be considered. Yet value presupposes an answer to the question: Of value to whom and for what? Values also presuppose a standard, a purpose, a need for action in the face of an alternative. The decision about so delicate and personal a problem as the separation of a retarded child from his family affects not only the life of the child but the lives of all those connected with him.

Regardless of the type of setting, be it a progressive modern rehabilitation center or an antiquated custodial institution, few, if any, preceding events in the life of a retarded are as traumatic as admission. Speech pathologists have agreed that patients display poor communication immediately following placement. Furthermore, it remains true that even aside from the question of whether an institution is the best place for a retarded child, it is difficult to house the increasing number of such children. Their number grows with population increase and with the lengthening of their life-span. It used to be that the average age at death of the severely retarded was twenty-eight. Now it is thirty-eight years. Sweden has solved the problem of overcrowded institutions, at least to some extent, by specialization. By law in that country children and adults must be kept separate. In our own country, some states ask fees for institutional care, these fees hopefully based on a family's ability to pay. Unfortunately, the fee basis is too often an inequitable one. Neither method solves the real problem of the overcrowded institution.

True, large state institutions cannot be run as private schools. Perhaps there should not be any large institutions. Perhaps there should be smaller, specialized institutions, and for the less severely retarded, home life with their families, with the community providing the counseling and training needed for the child's development. We ourselves believe that the solution lies within the community. Although foster home care is being provided by state aid this, too, must be increased. It must be supplemented with part-time care for emergency family situations. A community cannot wait until the states provide smaller institutions. Instead, it must make every effort to keep a child at home, even to the extent of providing financial assistance to those families who really need it.

Children kept at home must of course have periodic evaluations. This is already an accepted policy but one not too faithfully performed even in institutions. Too little time, too small a staff to give re-examinations, however, scarcely excuse the permanent institutionalizing of a child or adult who might have lived in his home and community.

"We just did not know what she could or could not do," said one mother of a severely retarded, cerebral-palsied girl. "We were oversolicitous, I know, but how could we be otherwise? No one told us that periodic medical attention was necessary. Now we've been told that because of the lack of proper attention she has contractions and atrophy of the hands, fingers, knees, and ankles. The physician has admitted that had we been able to receive service in our community during her preschool years she would probably be walking today."

Parents yearn to supply a child's needs and yet they must learn how to help the child help himself and thus *how to prevent love from becoming a stumbling block*. For example, cerebral damage is usually not limited to any single area of the brain and thus many associated physical defects may be found in addition to mental retardation. Approximately 50 percent of cerebral-palsied children are retarded and of these, half may have eye defects, many have hearing loss, and over 70 percent have some form of speech disorder.

The concept of home care and training of the retarded, under expert guidance, has never been fully explored; however, it is being extended as a result of the recommendations of the President's Panel on Mental Retardation. Communities wishing to provide special services to families of severely retarded children might find it valuable to investigate the United Cerebral Palsy of Pennsylvania's "Home Service Program." *

This includes special technical assistance in home care feeding, lifting, carrying, toilet training, adapting clothing to the needs of the person, bathing and a variety of similar problems. No fees are charged to handicapped persons or their families, and when specialized equipment is required, the Home Service Director assists in securing such service at the lowest cost to the family. Through both formal and informal meetings, techniques and methods of

* "Home Service to the Cerebral Palsied," United Cerebral Palsy Association of Pennsylvania, Harrisburg.

home care are given to nurses so that needed attention may be provided. Techniques being developed for cerebral-palsied retarded children could be used for all handicapped persons, and especially perhaps for the aged. Our industrial civilization has not yet solved the problems of the old, for whom it seems to have no place. The story is told that one beautiful spring day, after placing a few personal belongings into their one-horse trap, a robust Welshman and his father started out of the city down a winding coal-dust filled path. As they drove along chatting about friends and the weather, they came to a favorite stone bridge.

"Let us stop here for a while," the old man said. "I'd like to look around."

"Very well," his son replied and he pulled on the horse's reins.

They both climbed down, and seating themselves on the side of the top of the bridge, they looked out over the peaceful landscape. For miles the wide expanse of the valley unfolded before them. The silence was only broken by the gentle rippling of the stream below, when finally the son questioned, "Father, what are you thinking?"

"Son," replied the frail old man as he stroked his beard, "I was just remembering the time when I, too, stopped here with your grandfather on my way to take him to the county home."

Sound reasoning, statistics and personal knowledge tell us it would be regrettable if while planning for our aged population we do not profit by experiences given to us by our retarded children.

CHAPTER VIII

IMAGINATIVE LEADERSHIP

Among the lessons which our retarded have taught us is the value of able leadership, and in a democracy such as ours its value, like that of diamonds, is scarcity. Leadership is expensive because its price involves our most precious possessions—time and talent. Experience at the national, state and local levels has proved that leadership can never be provided entirely by legislation. It is not the result of appointment, neither can it be guaranteed by the prestige of birth, position, or money. Leadership is an inherent quality which must develop in and through individuals, and its roots lie in concern for the well-being of humanity.

Although leaders can be identified when they appear, it is often difficult to understand what comprises leadership. Perhaps this is because there are so many different kinds of leaders. Binet, through his concern for retarded children, became the founder of all psychological tests; Buddha, the religious guide of millions, understood the sorrow of mankind; Gandhi, the quiet persuasive one, assumed responsibility for the political needs of his people; Schweitzer, the musician, left home and family to heal the wounds of strangers in a foreign land. Each is a leader in his own right.

The acclaim given to leaders is based not only on what they personally accomplish, but the remarkable skill in human relations which they are able to develop. We measure their leadership by what they do for others, with others and to others; more precisely, by the manner in which they induce followers to unite in a common goal. Yet everyone possesses the ability of leadership in varying degrees. Each life, like a ripple in a stream, affects every person with whom it comes into contact. The scope of one's activity may not be as extensive as another's but the impact of a life, be it good or bad, has a profound and often lasting influence.

Then, too, each person falls into one of two classifications, at times a follower, at other times a leader, depending entirely on what he knows and does not know, or what he says and does not say. The underlying question is not in which group a person finds himself at a particular time, for both are necessary, but in the amount of responsibility he is willing to assume. As the character matures, the person becomes concerned not only with the needs of those he knows and cherishes but with others whom he may never see.

Consider the life of the Honorable Herman Robinson, member of the Tennessee State Senate. When he was born, doctors shook their heads sadly and agreed that he would never walk or talk and perhaps not live. Little did they realize that this baby, so afflicted with spastic paralysis, would by the time he was seven begin overcoming the multiple weaknesses of his body by attempting to communicate.

Learning to walk was a long, discouragingly monotonous process. Time after time he fell, until one miraculous day to the amazement of his family and friends he walked out of his wheelchair. Eventually with the help of sympathetic and understanding teachers, sounds which at first were unintelligible were replaced by words.

After high school he attended East Tennessee State College, and while there decided that he would become a newspaper reporter, but it was during the depression and jobs were scarce. Since he was so eager to learn and so willing to work, the local publisher finally agreed to hire him at the exorbitant salary of $2 a week. His duty was to sweep the office after working hours, but while there he began his apprenticeship as a writer, and it was through newspaper work that he became interested in politics.

His wife, his children, his friends and his associates all agree with him that it is not the handicap, but surrender to the handicap which hinders a man from becoming a leader. By 1963 he had served four consecutive terms in the Senate, elected for the last three without opposition. His motivation was strong, his courage exceptional, but neither compare to his service to others.

In Great Britain during World War II, Lady Reading, now a member of Parliament, organized the Women's Voluntary Services, an organization numbering over a million and a half workers. Once she sagely commented to us, "Leaders never say I, instead they say we. Leaders, however, use three I's. Imagination—to see a problem; Ingenuity—to know how to meet it; and Initiative—to work out the answer. As a leader you should not only be able to understand your followers, attempt to 'walk in their shoes,' but then, allow them to improvise their work in the way they can do it best. They, too, have creative abilities. It is essential for a planning body to set policy, but the details must be left to the ingenuity of others. This is important for two reasons; you can never cover all the emergencies which occur, and if others are accustomed to using their own imaginations, they will handle problems as they arise. Second, people want to have some free play or they lose interest and spirit in carrying out a job. Give them pride and pleasure in accomplishment. It is then a community enterprise. Everyone needs responsibility, but different people thrive on different amounts. Don't try to change someone else's character. Develop the best characteristics."

This concept of leadership is exemplary. It includes a vision of what others can do, but it is not visionary. It does not impose a pattern of thought and conduct, yet it helps others to discover and choose what they should do about a problem. In some countries the talented and fortunate have been trained to be responsible for the welfare of others. The basis for this was the belief that men were born to be either followers or leaders. If well born, it was assumed they possessed the qualities of leadership and that all others were of necessity followers. As members of a free nation, it is not only our privilege but our personal responsibility to provide for the development of every handicapped citizen in our community to the limit of his capacity. This we can only achieve if all unite in planning for and assisting with provision of their needs.

We Americans are a proud people. We are proud of our heritage, of our leaders, of our achievements. As an example to the world of what has been accomplished in less than three hundred years by persons living in a democratic society, much of our progress may be that we have been privileged to use that which we have considered best from the centuries of culture which preceded us. To supply our needs, both individually and collectively, we have combined customs, interests, policies, and objectives from many countries. This process of selectivity continues to influence governmental administration, business and labor management policies, professional and lay organizations, and, more recently, the integration of some of our health and welfare services.

Though our lives and activities are usually localized, we do think nationally. The University of Pennsylvania's Wharton School of Finance and Commerce, primarily concerned with instruction of its pupils, recently forwarded to Congress a comprehensive six-year analysis of the mutual fund industry. While the main purpose of this comprehensive report was to guide federal legislators, the facts as presented have already affected those in major financial circles and will no doubt have a distinct influence on owners of shares and prospective investors throughout the country. Again, labor's strength has resulted from the amalgamation of nationally common but individually local goals. Policies of professional and lay associations, though originally initiated by member organizations, formally come into being and practice only if and when approved by national boards.

Today, international policies and goals motivate individual thought and action. Any impasse that plagues foreign affairs involves us. It is not uncommon to hear a man on the street knowledgeably and provocatively discussing the miraculous economic powers which could result should agreement be reached by financial leaders on the acceptability of Common Market practices. As a result, we are becoming increasingly careful about the person whom we help select at the polls, be he responsible for local, state, or national affairs, because we recognize that acting on our behalf, he can materially alter our lives, the lives of our children, our friends, and those of generations to come.

Philanthropy in our country is under review for some of the same reasons. In 1961, financed by the Rockefeller Foundation and prepared by the Harvard University School of Public Health, a report of a two-year study of the nation's voluntary health and welfare agencies was published. Although this 88-page document included descriptive items about the achievements of many organizations, severe criticism was directed at those whom they believed to be operating in an "antiquated, patched-up and at times jealously self-centered" manner. The reporting panel, two of whose members were former Secretaries of Health, Education, and Welfare, declared that among the many questions being asked by the public about voluntary agencies were: "Are there too many? Are voluntary agencies really necessary in view of the great expansion of governmental health and welfare activities? How are they spending the funds which they collect from the public?"

Two major proposals were presented for the purpose of strengthening service to retarded and handicapped persons. They recommended appointment of a National Commission on Voluntary Health and Welfare Agencies, and that a system of uniform accounting and financial reporting for the agencies be devised. When assailed by representatives of some of these major organizations, Lindsley F. Kimball, former vice-president of the Rockefeller Foundation and chairman of the *ad hoc* committee, replied, "The committee was established in the first instance in response to very widespread, very urgent and very earnest and sincere pleas from troubled citizens from coast to coast. Twenty-one citizens were asked to serve on the committee and twenty-one accepted, and only because of their anxiety to strengthen the American way of voluntary giving." *

Recently, in its yearbook entitled "Giving, U.S.A.," the American Association of Fund Raising Council reports that we have reached a new high in giving. The grand total for 1962 was $9.3 billion, or $600 million more than was given in the previous year. Of this amount, $750 million was obtained as a result of campaigns sponsored either by our major independent health charities, the United Fund or Community Chest drives. Gifts from public-spirited individuals, by far the largest group of contributors, amounted to no less than $7.4 billion.

At a recent meeting conducted by a group of businessmen considering the selection of a campaign manager for their annual Community Fund Drive, one gentleman inquired, "Friends, in view of the staggering sums now being provided through governmental sources for health and welfare services, can we expect a leveling or diminishing of this progressively increased demand for personal dona-

---

* Lindsley F. Kimball, "Critics Stand By Their Guns On Gift Groups," New York *Herald Tribune*, August 2, 1961.

tions? My wife works too and so we are both expected to give at the office, and then we are expected to contribute during the house-to-house campaign. Where will it end?"

"Experts," one of the men replied, "tell me that our community needs are growing. I'm particularly interested in service. Some of us gravitate to certain organizations because of our own special needs. A few are particularly interested in United Cerebral Palsey, others in the Association for Retarded Children. I appreciate your interest, but Marie and I prefer to contribute only to members of the Community Chest."

"I know what you mean," exclaimed the largest fuel oil distributor in the group. "I don't mind giving but I do wish these agencies would coordinate their activities. We all have to work together. Why don't they? I don't mean just on fund raising. You mentioned experts—what do you mean?"

"Experts in the field of social health and welfare. Let Sam tell you. He understands—fact is, we were discussing it last night. It's a real problem. Nowadays, we live not only long enough to see our children develop into manhood, but also our grandchildren. The span of life covers three generations. When I was a child my parents didn't have so many community problems. The town I came from was small. It's different now, but Sam, you tell them."

Sam Silke took a long puff on his cigar, twisted his mouth, looked far off into the distance then began, "Fellows, you all know I'm biased. My girl is retarded. By 1970 our total population will be 214 million. Of course I'm speaking in terms of the whole country, but this is our country. You may not realize it, but thirty children out of every one thousand will be retarded. One-third of these will be preschool or school age. If we can provide proper social, educational and vocational training for them, they tell us we can expect some independence for twenty-five of these. Only four of them will become "semi-dependent" adults—that is, able to care for their personal needs and help at home with simple jobs. One will need nursing care. And"—he looked squarely at the man across the room—"Jim, one of every four beds at the state institution will be a . . ."

"Severely retarded crib case, you were going to say," the other put in. "And those figures don't include other handicapped persons such as the arthritics, muscular dystrophy patients or the emotionally disturbed.

"Sam hasn't yet told you what to expect, so I will. It is estimated that within seven or eight years voluntary support for an additional $2.5 billion will be required for necessary health and welfare services. We must find a better way to provide service right in our own community. This doesn't mean it will necessarily eliminate costs, because many present services are still inadequate and we all know that there are a few which should be initiated. We cannot nor must not depend entirely on the state. In some way a plan must be devised to consolidate, incorporate and improve the functions of our own agencies but in no way diminish their effectiveness. Don't ask me how—I don't know the answer."

For those of us who have accepted President Kennedy's daring challenge, "Our communities are what we make them," this means but one thing. We must devote more time to the encouragement of new leadership for the preservation of life-span services to the retarded in their own community. We must think imaginatively. This is the key which if shared with others and transferred into meaningful activity will open doors of possibility for our retarded. A leader must do, not just be.

CHAPTER IX

COORDINATED SERVICE

"We do not wish to mention coordination," said Dr. Leonard W. Mayo, chairman of the President's Panel on Mental Retardation, as he introduced the consultants to the members of Task Force VI on Coordination. "Far more can be done by an indirect approach. We prefer to consider how *to develop, strengthen, extend and arrange for improved relations among agencies.*" *

Though representative of the entire nation, the Panel discussed problems that were similar in many respects. Connecticut reported that because of a lack of central leadership to prevent a time lag in service, statutory authority had become necessary. "Statutory requirements lead to community services," said Bert Schmickel, Deputy Commissioner of Health. "We do not duplicate service, neither can we provide everything. We'll go as far as possible in day care service but the community *must* support its own

* Mayo, Leonard W., Unpublished Minutes of Task Force VI, President's Panel on Mental Retardation, 1962, p. 2.

state services. In the rehabilitation regional center we say, 'We will build the center but not staff it.' We must somehow guarantee that they contribute." *

On the other hand, Louisiana had authorization for day care centers but their policy was to say to a community: "If you will organize first and provide the staff, we will negotiate services but we must retain the final approval." **

Kentucky, a state in which there are fifty cabinet members, seven of which are involved with problems of the mentally retarded, organized a Division of Mental Retardation responsible to the Commissioner of Welfare in order to "encourage the development of programs in the areas of unmet needs. . . ." In Illinois, an Association of Retarded Children serving four counties through a Board of Directors and a Professional Advisory Committee, was developing a lifetime plan for mentally retarded. Because state services vary, communities are affected differently. Service in Minnesota was impeded by state attempts to set Health and Welfare standards to which agencies did not conform, one department could not enforce other organizations to act, each department had individual philosophies, competition was found among leaders, there was placement of mentally retarded with mentally ill, and there was a shortage of consultants.

Dr. Bernard Bucove, chairman of the Subcommittee on Mental Retardation, Washington Governor's Inter-Agency Committee on Health, Education, and Welfare Programs, reported that since there had been seven major agencies

---

* *Ibid*, p. 7.
** *Ibid.*, p. 7.

serving retarded, "a shuffling of agency responsibility" had prevented progress. "It took two years," he said, "before they were ready to meet with other agencies. When they realized they couldn't bring people together, they went to the governor with an idea of an Inter-Agency Committee on Mental Retardation for the purpose of exchanging information and developing a cooperative plan. Then it took four more years to educate the staff people and one year to establish a Demonstrative Community Project." *

A lag in activity existed in New York until 1956, at which time an Inter-Departmental Board was "created to initiate and execute programs dealing with health and mental health problems which concern more than one state department." At present, exceptional strides are being made by the Governor's Council on Rehabilitation. Despite the differences in geographical location or population distribution, each of these consultants agreed that services could only be improved if and when community leaders assume their responsibility. "For example," the New York representative said, "we need a fixed point so that extended parent counseling may be given, teaching services stimulated and a climate of acceptability induced for the understanding of legislative mandates. There still exists actual discrimination about parents. Services are sometimes provided to one child but denied another of equal need. Services should be provided on the basis of medical need and not by diagnostic category." **

Pennsylvania reported that a Governor's Committee for the Handicapped had been appointed for the purpose of

* *Ibid.,* p. 3.
** *Ibid.,* p. 4.

extending and improving life-span services to all handicapped persons. To survey unmet needs at the community
level and to relate as a partner in possible future action to
help meet these needs, the Committee invited Mayors of
nine cities to arrange for and personally conduct public
hearings. Information received indicated many common
community problems. It was apparent that innumerable
gaps in services existed both in rural and urban areas, and
that this was due to lack of trained personnel or facilities.
It was found that the multiplicity of services being provided by public and private agencies created confusion,
and some local concern was expressed about unwise use of
professional staff.

Following the local hearings, the Committee conducted
a separate one-day hearing for state public agencies and
one for state private agencies, after which they asked themselves the question, "Who, in the American community,
because of his position of leadership, can make the most
positive approach to problems of the handicapped and who
can be the most instrumental factor in implementing
services of statewide agencies?" The mayor. From an age
in which the role of mayors was limited mostly to protection of persons and property, street maintenance, and
community housekeeping, the moment this one person now
accepts the complexity of becoming our leading citizen he
assumes responsibility first, for our social well-being; and
second, the advancement of our economic growth. It is he
who must rely most heavily on experience—either self-
generated or job-generated—because the mayor is the heart
of our community.

To assist the communities, the Governor's Committee

for the Handicapped conceived a plan for local cooperative effort between lay citizens, professional persons, and
government in the form of Mayors' Committees for the
Handicapped. The aim of each was to integrate into the
life of the community every retarded or handicapped person *from birth to death,* reserving institutional care only
for those who, because of the severity of their handicapped
condition, could not remain at home.

"We believe," said the Pennsylvania representative, "this
plan benefits all citizens; for the handicapped by removing
the frustration of their lives, giving them opportunities to
develop themselves and be of use to others; for the so-called
normal citizens the satisfaction of their instincts for justice
and humane behavior." It can also be the means of developing a community climate of interest, acceptance and
active participation in the solution of local problems by
promoting wider use of public, private and voluntary organizations." *

In development of the plan it was recognized that since
community areas of service differ widely, leading citizens
appointed by the mayor or mayors of one or more cities,
or the county commissioners of one or more counties, were
requested to determine the community area which lent itself to efficient use and coordination of both public and
private agencies. In several localities where an existing
health and welfare council or similar organization was serving the handicapped, no such separate committee was
formed. In such instances, the mayor was requested to ap-
point someone to the existing group to act as his repre-

* *Ibid.,* p. 4.

sentative. This enabled the organization to receive his support for either ongoing or proposed programs.

"A good business leader," said one mayor faced with the problem of supplying the needs of the mentally retarded in his city, "picks the most likely men he can find, tells them what he wants them to do, and how he wants it done. He watches how they do it, corrects them when they are wrong, and tells them when they are right. In a factory, an inspector checks the items which might be considered rejects. I cannot do this. I deal with human lives. I can't afford to make mistakes or let my community make mistakes.

"It is difficult for anyone who has never really been hungry to understand how a starving person must feel. One who has never been ill seldom appreciates good health. My brother has a homebound retarded child, and although I realize I cannot fully appreciate his problems, I am deeply concerned about them. I want to help you so that these children and their parents can be provided with the things they need here in my community."

As a result of President Kennedy's extraordinary leadership for the mentally retarded and mentally ill, our public conscience has been aroused from its lethargy. Not satisfied with our initial response, Mr. Kennedy said dramatically in his message to Congress on February 5, 1963, "Services to both the mentally ill and to the mentally retarded must be community-based and provide a range of services to meet community needs." * The impact of his gravity gains vigor each time we see his words in print. "Community"

* Message from The President of the United States, 88th Congress, 1st Session, Document No. 58, p. 3.

takes on a new emphasis because he is speaking of our community, the place we call home, the locality in which our children live and where their problems and ours must be solved. It is for this reason, whether we live in a rural area, a small town, a suburban village, or a teeming metropolis, a sense of personal responsibility becomes even more deeply imbedded in our hearts.

Leaders are available and ready to help. As volunteers, we have been contributing money and time, yet we still find ourselves caught between a multiplicity of agencies— the Community Chests, United Funds, National and Local Health organizations. Their value to the community we dare not question. We know that innumberable gaps exist in the services, and statistics indicate that only 3 percent of all solicited monies can be attributed to false or irregular auspices. It is the need for new and improved local services that creates our widespread concern.

An objective analysis of our dilemma points to several underlying facts. Each voluntary or private health and welfare agency, be it local, state, or national, was designed originally to serve a particular group of citizens. Yet when organized, because of its special nature its functions appear to the public to be somewhat similar to those of other social welfare groups. This is very confusing particularly when program activities either support or supplement those of existing public agencies.

The tremendous impact of the parent-inspired National Association for Retarded Children, Inc., is but one example. From a slow local beginning in the 30's, through its formation fourteen years ago, this vast army of volunteers, now comprising over 1,000 individual chapters, has been the means of changing the lives of millions of children and parents alike. Today, though organized specifically to serve the retarded, like other national health and welfare agencies, it continues to relate its activities to the focus of the 1960 White House Conference on Children and Youth—promoting opportunities for children to realize their full potential in freedom and dignity.

Services and facilities vary in each community. Some parents have had to travel over a hundred miles to obtain a complete diagnosis and evaluation of their child's condition. Then to their dismay they find that recommended treatment is unavailable in their own town. Again, a parent may find, due to the needs of the child, that he requires the help of several private agencies. He may be a member of the local Association for Retarded Children, where he himself is receiving parent counseling, and at the same time the Society for Crippled Children and Adults, Inc., may be providing therapy for his preschool child. Another parent of a retarded child may be receiving therapy from the local affiliate of United Cerebral Palsy Associations, Inc., because therapists are so scarce in many communities.

Just as no one individual can be all things to all people, so no one single agency can be all things to all citizens. Certainly government agencies have clear obligations, yet state and national planning and the federal funds now being made available to communities are of little value unless they bear fruit in the form of strong community leadership. Retarded and handicapped persons are an inevitable part of any city or town. Thus, because there is no single solution to current personnel or facility shortages, the most logical starting point is within the community itself—right where the burden of disability creates human misery and where, due to specific individual needs, family funds are drained.

For the purpose of strengthening local agency services, in many communities Health and Welfare Councils or similar bodies are playing vital roles of leadership. The scope of their responsibility is wide in range, including, for example, research projects and service to dependent children, families, and the aging, as well as the control of juvenile delinquency and the conducting of various community surveys. Concerned as they may be with problems of the retarded, emotionally disturbed, and physically handicapped, some councils have insufficient staff or funds to devote much time to them. Acting as catalysts, they nevertheless perform an invaluable service by referring both individuals and families to appropriate member agencies.

Another factor which has contributed to problems of the retarded is lack of unified long-range community planning. Goals have been limited. This was one of the major objectives of Pennsylvania's Mayors' Committees for the Handicapped. In Erie, for example, the first to complete a community project, a county dental service was created. In Johnstown, the mayor extended the duties of his Committee for Employment of the Handicapped to include life-span services. The chairman and membership are now in the process of establishing a sheltered workshop for the greater Johnstown area. The administrator of the Bradford Hospital, another mayor's chairman, is supervising the conducting of services in a three-county rural area to increase promotion of phenylketonuria tests for newborn babies. A professor at Pennsylvania State University, who was then chairman of the Mayor's Committee in State College, and now president of the Pennsylvania Association for Retarded Children, initiated action to organize what is now a Community Counseling Service for Centre County.

As an example of the fact that fulfillment of a need itself is not always as important as the manner in which citizens are encouraged to meet their own needs is the dynamic development of community leadership in Scranton. In that so-called "depressed area," an artisan jeweler has been developing the long-range project initiated by a community-minded pastor and former chairman of the Mayor's Committee. These two men, so widely separated by individual interest, with the continued personal support of the mayor have stimulated and energized leadership to carry out a recommendation made long ago by the Lackawanna County Welfare Council "to improve present services by construction and maintenance of mutually needed facilities through extension of inter-relationships and joint use of funds." *

Like many thoughtful recommendations, this one lay dormant for seven years until courageous community leadership came from the Mayor's Committee. Today, Allied Services for the Handicapped, Inc., uniquely composed of eleven separate community agencies furnishing like or related services, is establishing a $1,100,000 Rehabilitation Center to serve a population of 850,000 in eleven counties

* "Recommendation of 1956 Committee, Lackawanna County Welfare Council," reported by Allied Services for the Handicapped, letter dated February 28, 1963, to Governor's Committee for the Handicapped, Harrisburg.

of northeastern Pennsylvania. Nonpartisan interest and support from city and state officials has resulted in the creation of a Scranton Health and Welfare Authority as a legally constituted body for the purpose of floating a bond issue to supplement federal and state monies for construction of the building. Meanwhile, as medical plans progress, the Welfare Council of Lackawanna County and COME-BACK, Incorporated, of New York City have been conducting an outstanding community recreational program for the aged.

These are only a few examples of what has been done in one state. More recently, Governor William W. Scranton established a Governor's Council for Human Services to mobilize all resources available under currently authorized programs in Pennsylvania. This council, among its many duties, is charged with responsibility for, and is now in the process of, developing a comprehensive plan to combat mental retardation. Already, fifteen task forces have been at work developing position papers involving the validity of present services as well as those which are needed. When completed, these reports will be editorially treated by professionals and made available to eight regional committees. The latter, in the meantime, are making service inventories of their region. Hopefully, all reports, including administrative, financial and legislative recommendations, when completed and combined into one, will constitute a long-range plan for the retarded which will be implemented at the state and local levels.

Similar activities are going on across the breadth and width of this nation. To some a long-range plan may well appear impractical. We believe, however, that it is necessary not because Congress has authorized appropriations to states to provide for such studies, but because of the ever-increasing needs of our retarded. We also believe goals may be possible to achieve if the public is made aware of them. This is *our joint responsibility.*

"Announcements which can be made this afternoon," said President Johnson as he greeted a number of his leaders, "reflect the pace of our progress. First, the National Institute of Child Health and Human Development has approved grants which will result in construction of two mental retardation centers, one on the East Coast, the other on the West Coast.

"Second, the Civil Service Commission has successfully begun a pioneering program for employing the mentally retarded, 85 percent of whom are employable. We are confident industry, like government, will find these people make capable, devoted workers at many levels.

"Third, the Advertising Council is making the subject of mental retardation their number one effort, a long step forward to awakening public awareness.

"Fourth, the United States Junior Chamber of Commerce is dedicating the energy and enterprise of its fine members to support of the program. . . . I believe we will accomplish more toward overcoming retardation in the next five years than the world has accomplished in the last five hundred years." *

The test of any society is the manner in which it cares for the handicapped. Under the Nazis, defective people

* President Lyndon B. Johnson, "Remarks of the President to the Kennedy Foundation Mental Retardation Group," The White House Rose Garden, June 15, 1964.

were the first to be eliminated and exterminated. Such a society, brilliant but ruthless, can destroy human compassion and eventually destroy itself. Especially in these days when we are concentrating on the discovery of brilliant minds, it is the retarded person who can keep alive within us the feeling and spirit of humanity. The person we should fear the most is the brilliant mind that is not humane. Federal and state leaders have set an example for us. They have challenged us to do our part within our own communities. Acknowledging and assuming personal responsibility is not enough. The touchstone must be continuity of effort. The retarded have taught us this.

CHAPTER X

SOCIETY'S RESPONSIBILITY

Jeremy Taylor once said: "No obligation to justice does force a man to be cruel, or to use the sharpest sentence. A just man does justice to every man and to everything; and then, if he be also wise, he knows there is a debt of mercy and compassion due to the infirmities of man's nature; and that is to be paid; and he that is cruel and ungentle to a sinning person, and does the worst to him, is in his debt and is unjust." *

Among all the lessons we have learned, or are learning from our retarded, by far the most important is that of a clearer understanding of justice, the ligament which holds civilized beings and civilized nations together. When honored, it becomes the foundation for social security, happiness, the basis of improvement and the progress of any society.

It was September. The last of the summer heat filled the

* Taylor, Jeremy, "Justice," *Useful Quotations A Cyclopedia of Quotations* (Grosset and Dunlap, New York, 1933), p. 310.

courthouse and frayed the nerves of its occupants. It was as if the day's events had been planned to stretch tempers to the breaking point. While waiting for the Juvenile Court judge to join them in his chambers, Mr. Anthony, the probation officer, incessantly drummed the table with the tips of his fingers and swung his right leg with such monotonous repetition that it even attracted the attention of the listless girl at his side. Her eyes continued to follow the movement of his foot until she finally asked, "You always do that?"

"Do what?" he inquired crossly.

"That drumming and jerking. Pa does it too. Teacher says it ain't nice."

"Be quiet. You have no respect for anyone. And, you'd better not say anything when Judge Kohn comes in—remember, speak only if told to speak."

"O.K.," Maude replied halfheartedly as they both became attracted by footsteps coming down the corridor.

Mr. Anthony stretched his legs and lazily rose to his feet to greet a longtime friend. "Morning, Judge," he said to the elderly, white-haired man who entered the room.

"Good morning, Tony." The judge walked quickly to the head of the table, shuffled some papers and then inquired, "What is this all about? Haven't much time. Let's get on with it. I have an appointment at the hospital, an important one, and you know the number of cases that are on the docket."

"This won't take long," Mr. Anthony replied. "You have my report. Maude, here, is a kid that's been going to the new Special Class. Lives with her stepfather. Mother's dead. Well, sir, it's like this. For weeks now she has been staying late after school. Her old man works in a garage afternoons and evenings. He didn't know about it. Finally, one of the boys in the high school was overheard talking about her. Said that she had been meeting his gang on the football field. Said they'd been having a ball. Not that it was costing them anything, but that she'd been giving them a quarter for messing around."

"Prostitution!" exclaimed the judge, glaring at the girl. "How old are you?"

Maude's eyes opened wide with fright but she did not reply.

"I repeat, how old are you?"

"Answer the judge," ordered the probation officer.

"Fifteen."

"Fifteen! A prostitute! Have you nothing to say for yourself?"

"No, sir," she said, disinterestedly. Her attention now had been caught by the buzzing of a large fly which kept going up and down the window in front of her.

"Nothing to say. What is happening to our youth? Tony, where is the teacher or that other woman, the supervisor, who usually comes here with you?"

"Supervisor's ill—in the hospital. Report is right there. I just didn't bother to tell the teacher—thought it would delay you. Remember how she went on last time about her pupils not being understood and all?"

"Do I? It is all very well to give these children a little leeway, but in a case like this, you're right."

At that moment Maude jumped to her feet and exclaimed, "I got it!"

"What have you got?" the judge angrily asked.

"The fly. Knew I could. Times they're hard to get, but I knew if I waited he'd come this way. They all do."

The two men looked at each other in disgust. Finally, they began laughing, each knowing what the other had thought at first. "Well," said the judge with finality, "that does it. Not fit. Ruins the lives of our boys. If I send her back to class she will only continue to carry on like this. Mayfair is the only place for her. I'll make the arrangements." A brief discussion of the plans followed and not long after, the judge rose to his feet. Not looking at the child, he shook hands with Mr. Anthony and left the room.

Maude was sentenced to Mayfair, a penal institution for women of childbearing age. Tragically, the girl had a mental age of a child of nine. She had lacked affection at home and understood very little of why she had been able to find a measure of happiness after school hours when one or two of the boys had agreed to kiss her for a mere pittance, considering it all a rare joke. Her stepfather, who had never wanted to keep her, was relieved when he learned of the developments.

It is a wonder that more children, be they members of rich or poor homes, do not become delinquent when lack of love and stifling boredom confine so many. One such instance is the case of a nine-year-old pupil of a public school Special Class for Educable Retarded, whose testimony in court provided evidence against his own mother. This boy, often left with the care of the younger children in the family, reported that his mother drank heavily. Simply but descriptively he told the court about the death of his four-year-old sister, how she had been severely

burned and placed naked into bed with two of the other
children. Although she was found dead by the mother
early in the morning, he reported that his mother had not
called for help until noon. During the two-day trial, the
defendant said that her daughter "always played with fire."
Review of the woman's case history indicated that several
years earlier she had pleaded guilty to a similar charge
after a ten-month-old daughter was found dead as a result
of what the court had termed "malnutrition and complete
neglect."

Another startling newspaper headline, "Ex-Grid Star
Sent to Prison in Armed Theft" underlines society's mis-
understanding of the needs of a retarded young man. His
was the story of a former Special Class student who at one
time was the community football star. While in school, his
friends and associates honored him, but, as the reporter
tersely concluded the brief item, "when he left school he
received no special applause. Perhaps it was too much of
a transition for him." Unwatched, unneeded, and uncared
for by the community, he began committing minor acts
of misdemeanor to attract attention. Finally, when ar-
raigned in court, it was for major charges—robbing a
service station attendant at gun point, self-administration
of narcotics, and burglary. When sentenced to serve from
five to ten years in a penitentiary on the charge of armed
robbery, should the community have taken its share of the
blame? One cannot but wonder what services had been
available to the retarded of that city. Obviously, school
was not enough. It never will be. Education for our retarded is but one of many services society must provide

its members. A just society endeavors to deal justly not only with those who are just to it but likewise to those who may for lack of service injure society.

— Throughout our country retarded and so-called "normal" children are frequently forced to remain in "temporary detention" for a year or more. The reason given for such treatment is that we lack adequate facilities for them. Many of these have committed only trivial offenses. A large number have done no wrong against society, but their fate is the same. Not unlike hundreds of neglected or dependent children, they are placed in jails for an indeterminate period and, while there, receive little if any educational service.

One emotionally disturbed girl of fifteen, who had run away from home and secretly married a parolee from a state penitentiary, became even more seriously disturbed because the probation officer forced his attentions on her while she was in his custody at the detention home. From there she was admitted to the State Hospital, where she remained for a three-month period of psychiatric care. Following discharge, she was placed in a foster home from which within a few weeks she was ousted by the foster parents because they could not handle her. Then, and only then, was she returned to her parents—but by that time they, too, could do little. Soon she ran away again. This time it was with a married man with several children. After a few weeks she left him, and now where is she, and what has society gained? The tragedy is that the court did not provide necessary out-patient psychiatric care—a recommendation which had been made by the psychiatrist. Instead, they considered the case if not closed, too difficult to handle.

"In our report to President Kennedy," said Dr. Leonard W. Mayo, chairman of the President's Panel on Mental Retardation, in November, 1962, "we asked that a separate report be prepared about the Mentally Retarded and the Law. I think this will be a classic. I can say that because I made no contribution to it except to encourage them to go ahead and try to find money outside of government for publishing their report. I think this will be a milestone in the field of the disabled and the law, not only because it says in clear terms that the mentally retarded have civil rights that must be protected, the same as the rights of anyone else, but because it says in clear terms that these people must be regarded as people first, and never as mentally retarded unless their degree of mental retardation means that they must have special attention.

"It will be a milestone not only because it goes into the whole admission policy of hospitals and institutions, but because it says in regard to mentally retarded and criminal law, unlike the law, or the practice of the law at least, that a mentally ill person *cannot tell* the difference sometimes between right and wrong. In many cases, and probably more often than not, the retarded person who is able to function in the community at all does know the difference between right and wrong, at least many times, perhaps most of the time, and therefore, he should not be excused per se on the grounds of his retardation! But, and this is important, his life, history, his functioning as a human being in a community, in the home, in school and at his work, when the degree of retardation can be diagnosed and explained, must be taken into consideration as a factor." *

During the course of their deliberations, Judge David L. Bazelon, chairman of the Task Force investigating these problems, and his colleagues discussed these delicate nuances with many government attorneys. Several persons, when interviewed, said that they were fully aware that retardation is a factor to be considered in its degree and relation to the life of the individual. "But," said one man, "if you are going to give special attention to a person who supposedly has an IQ of under sixty, what would you do with someone whose IQ is below seventy?"

The judge replied, "I think he should also have this special type of consideration."

"What about those who have been determined by psychologists to have an IQ under eighty?"

"They, too, should have special consideration."

"Well!" the man exclaimed. "Soon you will be saying this about all people."

"Precisely," Judge Bazelon replied.

Discussions between able citizens regarding mentally retarded persons force us to reconsider humane, scientific and functional basic principles that apply to all people in relation to care, research and law.

The introduction to the "Report of the Task Force on Law" of President Kennedy's Panel on Mental Retardation, which has now been published, is so succinct we wish to repeat it here:

* Mayo, Leonard, S.Sc.D., "Keynote Address," *Proceedings of the Third Pennsylvania Conference of the Governor's Committee for the Handicapped, Co-Sponsored with the Alfred I. DuPont Institute,* Harrisburg, November 26, 1962, p. 21.

The law must be able to recognize disabilities and to differentiate between them. It must take account of the provision which society already makes for its disabled members. It must be prepared to adapt to the problems and to take advantage of alternatives in disposition. Changes in scientific and professional understanding assist the law with the first problem. Changes in social organization and professional care possibilities provide the law with possible solutions to the second problem. *The third problem is the law's alone to solve.* It is part of its never-ending search for coherent legal principles with which to face continuously changing social conditions.*

Counselors agree that there is a necessity to provide special laws which may be applied to the mentally retarded and others of our society who are disabled in some way, but what is so difficult is the drafting of such legislation. Identification and classification of the *degree* of retardation must be specific and yet permit flexibility of interpretation. This implies a contradiction. As Dr. Elizabeth M. Boggs, vice-chairman of the Task Force on Law, and former President of the National Association for Retarded Children, once said to us, "Justice must reflect the purpose and function of the law, not merely some abstract definition of mental retardation." For years governments have been nation-minded, religions have been church-minded; labor unions have been union-minded, and educators, education-minded. Though all of these institutions have existed for the benefit of humanity as a whole, it is only

* "Introduction, De Minimis non curat Lex," *Report of the Task Force on Law, President's Panel on Mental Retardation* (U. S. Department of Health, Education, and Welfare, Public Health Service, January, 1963), p. 1.

recently that each group has recognized the importance of being "person-minded." It is the individual, with his very personal differences and needs, with whom each must deal if a program is to be effective. The same principle applies to legislation.

Let us assume that two children with the same degree of hearing loss were brought before the Juvenile Court, both with an IQ of 65. One had been deaf from birth. He had never had the privilege of hearing language. The other had been deafened at the age of seven and up to that time had been a part of the hearing world of sound, music, and conversation. Would it be fair to treat both alike? Or take the case of two twelve-year-old retarded children both with a mental age of an eight-year-old child. One had been living with his family—loved, respected, needed, and allowed to function as well as he could, neither pushed beyond nor deprived of the privilege of development. The other had been raised in an institution—confined, unwanted, unloved, and unneeded. Would it be just to give the same sentence for the identical misdemeanor to each child? Absolutely not. Their backgrounds are different. Their individual understanding and comprehension cannot be compared, much less their needs.

This is where the cold criteria of measurement fail. They do not include answers to the question of how a person functions in society. More important, such test scores are not infallible in their prediction of what a person will do under a different set of circumstances. Some retarded persons can learn to modify their behavior as a result of discipline. Others may never be able to distinguish between punishment and routine curtailment of their activity. One may be able to understand the result of a harmful act whereas another may be incapable of living beyond the moment in which the act is committed.

There is of course a minority of extreme cases in which there exists such a complete lack of responsibility for criminal acts as to make the protective provisions as well as the restrictions of the law mandatory not only for the person himself but also for society. We repeat, however, that in the case of the retarded these are in the minority.

It is for those who are capable of functioning in their own homes and in their own communities that justice must remove its dark glasses. This includes the necessity for frequent review of the interpretation of the law in light of new knowledge about retardation. It involves a better understanding and appreciation of the advancements being made by the allied services administering and serving the handicapped. Many persons who would have been considered "totally incompetent" prior to the advent of Special Classes are now accepted by the community as capable citizens. Not all these "educable" retarded have had the privilege of attending Special Classes in the junior and senior high schools. The great majority were not given the opportunity, but they are salary-earning, family-raising, tax-paying citizens. They are contributors to this nation's welfare and should be considered as such.

What about those classified as "uneducable," those whose functioning does not permit them to pay taxes, and yet who are quite capable of enrollment in "trainable" classes? These boys and girls, young men and women, if given a chance can learn to take care of themselves. Does the average jurist understand the difference between these two groups, both of whom are mentally retarded? Among President Kennedy's major contributions to the world was his untiring effort to promote a public awareness and an understanding of these differences, because he knew that unless a person's abilities could be understood his needs would not be met. Even in the due process of law, until all who participate mutually understand the same expressions used to describe retarded persons and can ably communicate with one another, no judge will be able to protect individual rights or conduct the court's activities with mercy.

For example, when final arrangements for the guardianship of a person are being made, that person should be permitted to be present unless he is excused by the court for a just cause. In such a case his absence should be included in the report, and plenary guardianship reserved for only those who are determined to be incapable of selfmanagement and care. These are the sorts of things we as members of a nation dedicated to liberty and equality must demand.

Among the many task forces now preparing state comprehensive mental retardation plans, those dealing with the law are in the process of considering the most effective way to solve these legal problems. More encouraging, they concur that some of our present laws must be amended. To assist them in their deliberations, a checklist of state laws and regulations has been published by the Subcommittee on State Laws in Mental Retardation of the Advisory Committee to the Office of the Special Assistant to the President for Mental Retardation, Dr. Stafford L. Warren.*

It is, however, not enough for us to expect that those who draft, pass, and enforce laws should be responsible for their faithful implementation. We, too, have a responsibility. It is the same for any person when and if admitted to an institution be he retarded, mentally ill, or one who has committed a crime against society. We must insist that he be given the right to have his individual problems reviewed from time to time by a qualified team of experts to determine when and whether he is capable of return to his home and community. This applies to any person regardless of age.

If we do not accept our responsibility in such matters we then become guilty of injustice, for the principle of justice includes the principle of love and benevolence to individual man.

* "State Laws and Regulations Affecting the Mentally Retarded," U. S. Department of Health, Education, and Welfare, Public Health Service, Washington, D. C. June, 1964.

CHAPTER XI

THEIR GIFT TO US

What then, above all, has been their gift to us?

The intangible quality of love.

The ability to love is the generic center of growth in the human being. Without the ability to love we human beings degenerate into creatures less than ourselves. When we say we love we do not mean only the specific love for one fellow human or one's own family, or even for one's community, local or national. We mean that sensitivity of the heart, that awareness of the spirit, which is ready to go to work at any time for the benefit of other human beings, that yearning for justice and mercy for all. Yet the capacity to love begins with the love of a special person. The little child's first experience of love for his mother helps him to love his father, his brothers and sisters, and his friends. Similarly, the agonizing special love that parents feel for the retarded child opens their hearts to all such children, and sensitizes them finally to all human creatures.

Yet the ability to love must be taught. It is best taught

in childhood through love in the home and family and the final lesson is learned through suffering. Not everyone can learn to love through suffering. The most exacting test of the human being is in how he endures suffering, and there is no suffering more intense than the pain of knowing that one's child is retarded and without hope for development. Parents receive the evil news in two ways. They may reject or accept the experience. If they reject, they place the child in an institution and try to forget him. They write him off as a total loss. They eliminate him from their lives and thoughts and hearts, or they try to do so. Instead of resolving to live with and through the experience, enlarging their own lives thereby and encouraging the child by their love to reach his highest development, they try to eliminate feeling—an impossibility, for they have feelings of guilt, disappointment, and resentment far more destructive to their personalities than the original sorrow. Indeed sorrow itself is softened if there be love. Accepting the child for what he is, rejoicing in his slight improvements and little achievements, their hearts and minds are moved and widened toward all human beings and their frailties.

Yes, it might be better if these hopeless defectives did not live, and yet who dares to begin the process of elimination? For death is the least of the evil. The damage is done to the killer, not to the killed. For those who kill harden their hearts not only to the killed but to life itself. They are on guard against feeling anything for anyone. Human suffering does not move them. They steel themselves against feeling, and when feeling is dead the human being is no longer human. He becomes a sinister and destructive force.

Yet the damage is less to the child than to the family.
For we have seen what a retarded child can do in a family
where he is loved and accepted. He makes the hearts tender, the hearts of his parents and his brothers and sisters.
He teaches them lessons of patience and consideration,
those qualities so essential for every good human relationship. He teaches them that each member has his rights,
however weak the member, and this lesson, too, is essential
if we are to live together in the world with justice and
mercy for all. We are not born equal in this world. Some
are strong and some are weak. Our equality lies only in
the right, for each of us, to grow to our full capacity, whatever it is. And that there may be this equality, the strong
must bear the burdens of the weak, not only for the sake
of the weak, but for the sake of all. So in a family where
there is a retarded child, it is essential for the sake of all,
for the very principle of justice itself, that the retarded
child have his share of love and opportunity in the family.

And what is the community but the enlarged family?
A community, if it is to be a healthy and happy place for
everyone, must also be healthy and happy for the retarded
child, the weakest and most helpless. And by providing
the atmosphere in which he can grow, we provide the atmosphere for all to grow. We do not believe in segregating
the retarded child from other children. Let the normal
child understand that all are not as fortunate as he. Let
the normal child learn to be grateful that by chance it is
he who is strong, and let him learn to use his strength for
the less fortunate.

The ancient fifth commandment, "Honor they father
and thy mother that thy days may be long upon the land

which the Lord thy God givest thee," is a commandment that has been obeyed by ancient peoples who are still strong today. The continuing life of the Chinese, for example, is based upon this precept. Their acceptance, too, of the defective person in their families is part of their total acceptance of the human being as he is. What Communism has done to change this habit of mercy we do not know, but if it is changed then the seeds of destruction have begun in China, too. Once the barrier between life and death is torn down, none is safe. Once love and respect for the human being, whatever his state, is exchanged for ruthlessness, none is safe.

And what folly to think that one can forget a child by putting him in an institution while he is a baby!

"Our doctor says it would be better for all of us if we put our mongoloid baby boy into an institution as soon as we leave the hospital," a father said. "But I wonder if he is right?" the mother added.

"We think you would be wrong," we replied. "You would rob your little boy of the early environment to which he is entitled since he was born into your family— yes, even as he is, it is still his right, for it was not his fault any more than it is yours that the chromosomes he inherited are in faulty arrangement. Yet he is not defective in every way. He can feel the warmth of your love, he can respond. He would know in his own fashion in the institution where you put him that something was lacking. It is love that would be lacking. He will be washed and fed and cared for, the necessities of physical life will be provided, but without love he will never reach his best.

"Perhaps, you will say, his best is not high enough to be

concerned about. Then let us tell you that you too would never reach your best because you had not given yourself the opportunity to fulfill your natural instincts for love. You would have missed the experience of loving your retarded child and to that extent you would diminish your own growth. You will not be the man or the woman you may become unless you take this child to your heart where he belongs and keep him in your own home as long as possible. Yes, the day may come sooner or later when you will be compelled to put him in an institution, but you can do it then with peace in your hearts and minds, because you have done all you can. And he will have been a better child, happier in his new environment, more teachable, a better friend to other children like himself, because he will have had the foundation of love in his family and his home. And your other children, too, will have had the benefit of learning how to live with and how to love a child not like themselves, so that later in life they will be kinder and better people themselves, more just and more merciful. All this you will miss if you rob your child of love and home."

. . . Here ends our little book, upon the powerful theme of human love, the all-pervading spirit which alone makes tolerable this existence upon a globe imprisoned in time and space. We are here, we human beings, we know not how nor why. We are here and we are gone. In the brief span only love can serve, and we propose that the retarded child provides an essential means toward universal love. For the unit in any community is the family, and when the family of a retarded child receives him as a special gift, heartbreaking, yes, and at first crushing, but special and calling for special understanding and special love, that family becomes a focal point of leadership in the community, the parents leading the children in the atmosphere of love, and the family leading other families in the atmosphere of love, until the whole community is the better for the experience. Love enlarges the heart so that what is done for one small retarded child will have its rippling repercussions in benefits for other damaged children and handicapped persons, and thus warmth and mercy and justice for the one and the few will extend to all. The family is the unit of the community, the community is the unit of the nation, and the nation is the unit in the world of human society. It is not too much to say that what one family does with and for its retarded child in time may change the world.

INDEX